Work effectively in accounting

Workbook

Michael Fardon

osborne
BOOKS

Published by Osborne Books Limited
Unit 1B Everoak Estate
Bromyard Road
Worcester WR2 5HP
Tel 01905 748071
Email books@osbornebooks.co.uk
Website www.osbornebooks.co.uk

Design by Laura Ingham
Cover and page design image © Istockphoto.com/Petrovich9

Printed by CPI Antony Rowe Limited, Chippenham

British Library Cataloguing in Publication Data
A catalogue record for this book is available from the British Library

ISBN 978 1905777 990

Contents

How to use this book

Performance Criteria coverage by the Practice activities

Practice activities

Practice activities – answers

Practice assessments

Practice assessments – answers

Acknowledgements

The publisher wishes to thank the following for their help with the reading and production of the book: Alison Aplin, Maz Loton and Cathy Turner.

The publisher is indebted to the Association of Accounting Technicians for its help and advice to our author and editors during the preparation of this text.

Author

Michael Fardon has extensive teaching experience of a wide range of banking, business and accountancy courses at Worcester College of Technology. He now specialises in writing business and financial texts and is General Editor at Osborne Books. He is also an educational consultant and has worked extensively in the areas of vocational business curriculum development.

How to use this book

what this book covers

This book has been written specifically to cover the AAT Level 2 Learning Area 'Work Effectively in Accounting and Finance' which is based on a single QCF Unit:

■ Work Effectively in Accounting and Finance

The book has been written specifically to prepare students for the new AAT Computer Based Assessment which is being introduced from the end of September 2012.

what this book contains

■ **Practice activities – coverage of Performance Criteria**

The practice activities in this book have been based on the sample assessment material produced by AAT (see the MyAAT section of the AAT website www.aat.org.uk) and expanded to include extra questions on the AAT computer-based question model.

Instead of organising the short practice activities strictly in chapter order, this text bases the activities on the order of the performance criteria. Tutors and readers will find, however, that the running order of the activities very much mirrors that of the chapters in the Tutorial text.

The practice activities in this book are mapped against the individual Performance Criteria on the next page.

■ Three new **Practice assessments** are included to prepare the student for the Computer Based Assessments. They are based directly on the structure, style and content of the sample assessment material provided by the AAT at www.aat.org.uk. Suggested answers to the Practice assessments are set out in this book.

further information and resources

If you want to know more about our products, please visit www.osbornebooks.co.uk, email books@osbornebooks.co.uk or telephone Osborne Books Customer Services on 01905 748071.

Performance Criteria coverage by the Practice activities

Practice activities and Assesment Criteria covered

Practice activities		Performance Criteria
1	The accounting function in the organisation	1.1
2	Smooth running, solvency and legal compliance within an organisation	1.2
3	Reporting lines within an organisation	1.3
4	Policies and procedures within an organisation	1.4
5	Working with numbers	2.1
6	Communication skills - use of correct grammar	2.1
7	Communication skills - letters and emails	2.2
8	Report writing - report structure	2.2
9	Report writing - report contents	2.2
10	Managing the workload, scheduling and the effects of non-completion	3.1, 3.2
11	Dealing with conflicts and dissatisfaction at work	3.3
12	Continuing Professional Development	4.1, 4.2

Work effectively in accounting

Practice activities

1 The accounting function in the organisation

Task 1.1

The Departments in the list on the left-hand side are provided with accounting information by different sections of the Accounts Department. Match the types of information on the right-hand side with the appropriate Department on the left. Draw lines as appropriate.

Department needing information   **Type of accounting information**

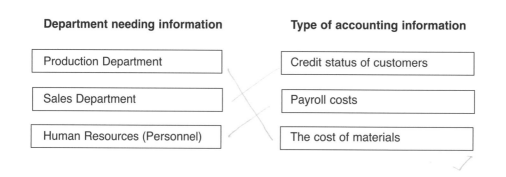

Department needing information	Type of accounting information
Production Department	Credit status of customers
Sales Department	Payroll costs
Human Resources (Personnel)	The cost of materials

Task 1.2

There are three main types of accountant. Match the types of activity listed on the right-hand side with the appropriate type of accountant on the left. Draw lines as appropriate.

Type of accountant   **What the job involves**

Type of accountant	What the job involves
Financial accountant	Checking on financial procedures
Management accountant	Reporting past financial performance
Auditor	Preparing financial forecasts

Task 1.3

Which of the following accounting tasks is **not** part of the costing function? Choose **one** option.

	✔
calculating the cost of products	
recording production data such as hours worked	
preparing sales reports for management	✓
preparing production reports for management	

Task 1.4

Which of the following accounting tasks is part of the purchasing function in a business? Choose **one** option.

	✔
recording customer orders, issuing invoices, receiving credit notes	
recording orders made by the business, receiving invoices, receiving credit notes	✓
recording orders made by the business, issuing invoices, receiving credit notes	
recording customer orders, issuing invoices, issuing credit notes	

2 Smooth running, solvency and legal compliance within an organisation

Task 2.1

Identify which of the following will encourage the smooth running of an organisation and which will make no difference to its efficiency. Tick the appropriate column for each line.

	Improves smooth running ✔	Makes no difference ✔
A Disciplinary Procedures document		✓
A 'green' policy of recycling paper		✓
A staff holiday plan to even out absences	✓	
A manual of accounting procedures	✓	
A weekly fire evacuation drill		✓

Task 2.2

Identify which of the following will help the solvency of an organisation and which are required for legal compliance reasons. Tick the appropriate column for each line.

	Solvency ✔	Legal compliance ✔
Paying employee income tax deductions to HMRC		✓
Avoiding having to pay overtime to employees	✓	
Making sure credit customers pay up on time	✓	
Completing the VAT Return for HMRC		✓
Completing the VAT Return on time to avoid a fine	✓	

Task 2.3

Indicate with a tick in the appropriate column below which aspect of running a business best describes the activities listed in the left-hand column. Choose from:

(a)   ensuring the smooth running of a business

(b)   improving the solvency of a business

(c)   compliance with legal requirements by the business

	smooth running ✔	improving solvency ✔	legal compliance ✔
Reporting on late payments to suppliers	✓		
Chasing up payments due by customers		✓	
Banking cheques payable to the business promptly		✓	
Carrying out a bank reconciliation statement	✓		
Insuring the company cars			✓
Paying the National Insurance Contributions of employees to HMRC			✓

✓

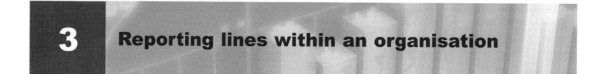

3 Reporting lines within an organisation

Task 3.1

The three people listed in the left-hand column of the table below work for Timon Limited:

Tommy Wong (Accounts Manager)	*Finance Director*
Anna Graniello (Chief Cashier)	*Accounts Manager*
David Schofield (Payroll Assistant)	*Payroll Line Manager*

Enter in the right-hand column the person to whom they are most likely to report. ✓

Choose this person from the following list:

Managing Director

Finance Director

Payroll Line Manager

Accounts Manager

Sales Supervisor

Costing Manager

Task 3.2

An accounts assistant working in the Costing Section of a business will **normally** report to (indicate the correct option):

✔

the Costing Manager only	
the Costing Manager and Production Manager only	
the Costing Manager and Production Manager and appropriate people in other departments of the business	✓

✓

4 Policies and procedures within an organisation

Task 4.1

Organisational policies and procedures are defined as (choose **one** option):

	✔
regulations imposed by law which must be adopted by an organisation	
regulations set up by an organisation which must be adopted by that organisation	✓
the terms relating to the sales of goods and services by an organisation	
a contract of employment issued by an organisation	

✓

Task 4.2

Which **two** of the following policies and procedures are most likely to be relevant to the accounting function?

	✔
grievance procedures for staff complaints	✓
environmental policy	
quality control in manufacture	
emergency procedures for suspected letter bomb	✓

✓

5 Working with numbers

Task 5.1

Round the following figures to the nearest whole number:

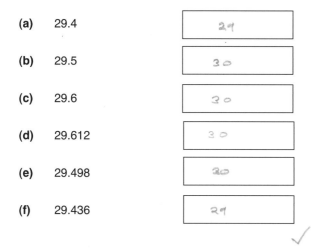

(a)   29.4 — 29

(b)   29.5 — 30

(c)   29.6 — 30

(d)   29.612 — 30

(e)   29.498 — 30

(f)   29.436 — 29

Task 5.2

Round the following figures to two decimal places:

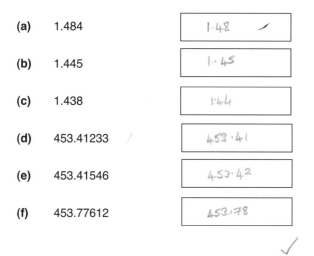

(a)   1.484 — 1.48

(b)   1.445 — 1.45

(c)   1.438 — 1.44

(d)   453.41233 — 453.41

(e)   453.41546 — 453.42

(f)   453.77612 — 453.78

Task 5.3

A fraction, percentage and a ratio are different ways of stating the proportion of parts to a whole, for example the number of female students in an accounting class.

If a class of 18 had 12 females and 6 males, the proportion of females would be:

(a)   as a fraction of the class

$2/3$ ✓

(b)   a percentage of the class
rounded to the nearest number

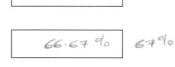 66·67 % 67%

(c)   the ratio of females to males
in the class

2:1 ✗ 2:3 ?

Task 5.4

You ask 40 people to a party but only 10 arrived within the first hour.

Express this number of guests who came as:

(a)   a fraction of the people invited

$1/4$ ✓

(b)   a percentage of the people invited

25% ✓

(c)   the ratio of people who came
to those who stayed away

1:3 ✓

Towards the end of the party another 5 guests arrive, saying that their taxi did not turn up on time. No other guests arrived.

Express the final total number of guests at the party as:

(d)   a fraction of those invited

$3/8$ ✓ $15/40$

(e)   a percentage (to one decimal place)
of those invited

37·5% ✓

(f)   the ratio of people who came
to those who stayed away

3:5 ✓

Task 5.5

You are given some receipts to process for petty cash. They include the amount paid but do not show the VAT amount. You are to calculate the VAT content and enter the VAT figure and the net amount (before VAT) in the table below.

	amount on receipt £	VAT amount £	net amount £
(a)	12.00	2·00	10·00
(b)	5.76	0·96	4·8
(c)	10.74	1·79	8·95

Task 5.6

You are asked to add VAT @ 20% to the following invoice amounts and calculate **the final total**. No discounts are involved. You should round down the VAT amounts to the nearest pence.

(a)   £1,200.50   1440·60

(b)   £456.24   547·48

(c)   £12.99   15·58

Task 5.7

You are issuing three invoices to customers to whom you allow settlement discount at 5%. The invoices also require the addition of VAT at 20%. The amounts shown are the totals after the deduction of trade discount. VAT should be **rounded down** to the nearest pence. Enter the **VAT** and the **final invoice total** of the three invoices in the table below.

	total amount £	VAT charged £	final invoice amount £
(a)	1,250.00	237·50	1487·50
(b)	495.20	94·08	589·28
(c)	845.60	160·66	1006·26

Task 5.8

You work as an Accounts Assistant for Belloptics Limited, a manufacturer of spectacles and sunglasses.

Your Accounts Manager has asked you to compile and process sales figures for the five Sales Managers who operate in the UK. This is not only so that she can compare their performance but also so that their monthly sales commission of 5% can be calculated.

The sales figures are for a four week period and do **not** include VAT @ 20%.

The figures are as follows:

Sales Manager	Week 1 £	Week 2 £	Week 3 £	Week 4 £	Total £
Briggs	5,450	16,975	8,291	13,175	43,891
Lucas	9,632	12,197	3,046	12,316	37,191
Patel	8,705	10,114	9,277	11,207	39,303
Hartmann	7,812	12,093	10,630	12,951	43,486
Ponti	8,361	10,176	12,950	16,230	47,717
Totals	39,960	61,555	44,194	65,879	211,588

You are to:

(a) Total the sales for each Sales Manager for Weeks 1 to 4. Enter the figures in the right-hand column of the table.

(b) Total the sales for each week and enter the figures in the bottom row of the table.

(c) Total the four figures in the bottom row and enter the total in the bottom right-hand box of the table.

(d) Now check your accuracy by totalling the first five figures in the right-hand column. This total should be the same as the total in the bottom right-hand box of the table. If there is a difference, you will need to check your workings.

(e) You now need to calculate the commission for each Sales Manager.

This is worked out at 5% of the sales figure excluding VAT to the nearest pound.

Enter the sales total in the second column and the commission to be paid in the third column.

Sales Manager	Total sales £	5% Commission due work to nearest £	
Briggs	43,891	2194.55	2195
Lucas	37,191	1859.55	1860
Patel	39,303	1965.15	1965
Hartmann	43,486	2174.30	2174
Ponti	47,717	2385.85	2386 ✓

(f) Your manager notices that Lucas has included VAT @ 20% in his sales figure. This has inflated the figure, which should not contain the VAT charged.

She asks you to recalculate his sales figure by removing the VAT. She suggests the easiest way of doing this is by multiplying the amount including VAT by the 'VAT fraction' of one sixth, ie $\frac{1}{6}$, and then recalculating the commission at 5%.

Carry out the calculation and enter your results in the table below. Work to the nearest pence for all the figures, except for the revised commission figure which should be rounded to the nearest pound.

	£	
Original amount including VAT	37,191	
Minus VAT content (amount x $\frac{1}{6}$)	– 6198.50	
Correct net sales total for Lucas	30,992.50	
Revised commission @ 5%	1549.63	1550 ✓

(g) Your manager asks you for the amount of the error as she wants to speak to Lucas about it.

The error amounts to: £ 810.00 ✓

6 Communication skills – use of correct grammar

Task 6.1

Its or It's? Study the four sentences below and tick the **two** correct options.

	✔
Its time to study.	
It's time to study.	✓
I hate this pasta; I do not like it's taste.	
I hate this pasta; I do not like its taste.	✓

Task 6.2

Its or It's? Study the four sentences below and tick the **two** correct options.

	✔
It's been raining non-stop for two weeks.	✓
Its been raining non-stop for two weeks.	
I love this carpet; I really like it's colour.	
I love this carpet; I really like its colour.	✓

Task 6.3

Its or It's? Study the four sentences below and tick the **two** correct options.

	✔
Its been ages since I saw you.	
It's been ages since I saw you.	✓
I like this coffee; it's aroma is very strong.	
I like this coffee; its aroma is very strong.	✓

Task 6.4

Its or It's? Study the four sentences below and tick the **two** correct options.

	✔
I like your perfume, its scent reminds me of roses.	✓
I like your perfume, it's scent reminds me of roses.	
I am glad I met you; its been a great evening.	
I am glad I met you; it's been a great evening.	✓

Task 6.5

There, their or they're? Study the three sentences below and tick the correct option.

	✔
There are many textbooks available.	✓
Their are many textbooks available.	
They're are many textbooks available.	

Task 6.6

There, their or they're? Study the three sentences below and tick the correct option.

	✔
Have the students taken there assessments yet?	
Have the students taken they're assessments yet?	
Have the students taken their assessments yet?	✓

Task 6.7

There, their or they're? Study the three sentences below and tick the correct option.

	✔
The students are sure that there competent.	
The students are sure that they're competent.	✓
The students are sure that their competent.	

Task 6.8

There, their or they're? Study the three sentences below and tick the correct option.

	✔
It's there problem, not mine!	
It's they're problem, not mine!	
It's their problem, not mine!	✓

Task 6.9

Two, too or to? Study the three sentences below and tick the correct option.

	✔
This curry is far two hot for me!	
This curry is far too hot for me!	✓
This curry is far to hot for me!	

Task 6.10

Two, too or to? Study the three sentences below and tick the correct option.

	✔
These questions make me go two sleep.	
These questions make me go too sleep.	
These questions make me go to sleep.	✓

Task 6.11

Two, too or to? Study the three sentences below and tick the correct option.

	✔
Two much double-entry is bad for your health.	
Too much double-entry is bad for your health.	✓
To much double-entry is bad for your health.	

Task 6.12

Two, too or to? Study the three sentences below and tick the correct option.

	✔
Two is company, three is a crowd.	✓
Too is company, three is a crowd.	
To is company, three is a crowd.	

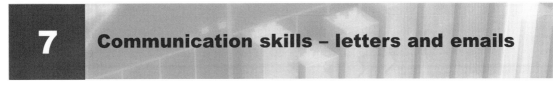

7 **Communication skills – letters and emails**

Task 7.1

Your name is Charlie and you work as an assistant in the Accounts Department of Gerrard Sportsgoods and have been passed the draft email (shown below) to complete.

The email is a request to Ayan Banerjee (a.banerjee@gerrardsportsgoods.com), an assistant in the Production Department, to provide details of 'Anfield' footballs manufactured during the month of July. You need the information by 2 August. You are to:

(a)   Insert the email address of the recipient in the appropriate box.

(b)   Complete the remaining boxes (they are numbered for reference) with the most appropriate words or phrases from the lists shown below (also numbered for reference).

From	c.brooks@gerrardsportsgoods.com
To	*a. banerjee@gerrardsportsgoods.com* ✓
Subject	*Manufacturing data for July* **1**

Hi Ayan

Please send me the quantity of   *'Anfield' footballs* **2** ✓   manufactured

during the month of   *July*   **3** . We need this information to carry

out a costing exercise. I need the information, please, by   *2nd August* **4** .

Many thanks and kind regards

Charlie

Accounts Department

Option Lists
Pick one word or phrase for each numbered box from the following numbered lists:

1   Manufacturing data for July, August data, Manufacturing data for August, Footballs

2   footballs, July footballs, 'Anfield' footballs, sports goods

3   May, June, July, August

4   2 May, August, 2 July, 2 August

Task 7.2

You have been passed the following draft letter (to a Mrs Clinton) to check.

There are five major errors which could include wrong spellings, bad grammar or wrong use of words.

You are to:

(a) Identify the five incorrect words and enter them in the left-hand column of the table below.

(b) Enter your correction of these five words on the appropriate line in the right-hand column of the table below.

Dear Miss Clinton,

Credit card referral

We have been advised by Worldpay that a purchase for £65.00 made by you on 13 July has been refused by your credit card company.

We recomend that you make a seperate payment to us by cheque or bank transfer so that we can fulfil your order. Their both acceptable methods.

Yours faithfully,

---

incorrect word	correction	
Mier	Mrs	✓
recomend	recommend	✓
seperate	seporat	✓
their	they are	✓
faithfully	sincerely	✓

8   Report writing – report structure

Task 8.1

A business report normally contains seven sections, each with a distinct function. The seven sections are:

Title, Summary, Introduction, Findings, Conclusions, Recommendations, Appendices

You are to match the two sections on the left with the appropriate descriptions on the right. Draw two lines as appropriate.

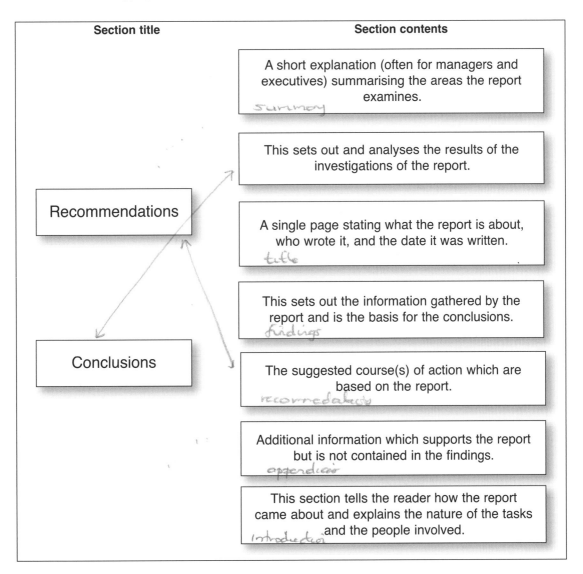

Section title	Section contents
	A short explanation (often for managers and executives) summarising the areas the report examines. *Summary*
	This sets out and analyses the results of the investigations of the report.
Recommendations	A single page stating what the report is about, who wrote it, and the date it was written. *title*
	This sets out the information gathered by the report and is the basis for the conclusions. *findings*
Conclusions	The suggested course(s) of action which are based on the report. *recommendations*
	Additional information which supports the report but is not contained in the findings. *appendices*
	This section tells the reader how the report came about and explains the nature of the tasks and the people involved. *Introduction*

9 Report writing – report contents

Task 9.1

Ella, the Human Resources Manager at Mercato Limited, has been receiving feedback from staff in the Accounts Department who are becoming dissatisfied with their lack of promotion.

Ella contacts the Accounts Department Manager and they decide to organise a staff survey and a series of interviews to find out about levels of motivation and the need for staff training. The report which they produce will help them in their CPD (Continuing Professional Development) planning and the making of recommendations for the staff.

The results of their investigation are set out in the table below. 50 members of staff were interviewed.

The areas being investigated were graded in three levels: 'Good', 'Fair' and 'Poor'.

RESULTS OF STAFF CPD QUESTIONNAIRE			
Question	**Good**	**Fair**	**Poor**
How do you rate your motivation for doing your current job?	7	23	20
How do you rate the training you are given in your job?	4	22	24
How do you rate your opportunities for promotion?	3	27	20

(a) Convert the figures in the above table to percentages of the total number of responses and complete the table below. Remember that there were 50 members of staff interviewed altogether.

RESULTS OF STAFF CPD QUESTIONNAIRE			
Question	**Good %**	**Fair %**	**Poor %**
How do you rate your motivation for doing your current job?	14	46	40
How do you rate the training you are given in your job?	8	44	48
How do you rate your opportunities for promotion?	6	54	40

(b)   Select **TWO conclusions** to be included in the report. Tick the appropriate boxes.

	✔
The results for motivation and promotion opportunities were both excellent.	
The result for motivation was less positive than the result for promotion opportunites.	
The worst result related to the quality of staff training.	✓
There is no real reason for changing the present training system.	
All areas of CPD (motivation, training and promotion) need urgent attention.	✓
Staff seem very happy with the present system of training and promotion.	

(c)   Select **TWO recommendations** to be included in the report. Tick the appropriate boxes.

	✔
Reduce the number of staff so that there will be more opportunity for individuals to go on training courses.	
Review and expand the training programmes so that there is more opportunity for improving staff performance and motivation.	✓
Schedule and carry out CPD interviews with all members of staff so that individual needs are fulfilled and motivation improved.	✓
Reduce the frequency of staff interviews so that they will have less opportunity to complain and get demoralised.	

10 Managing the workload, scheduling and the effects of non-completion

10.1 If you find that you are falling seriously behind with your work and cannot meet a deadline you should (choose the most appropriate option):

	✔
tell your line manager	✓
not tell your line manager	
tell a colleague that he/she should help you	
say you have a bad headache and you need to go home	

✓

10.2 In which of the following circumstances are you likely to need to change the priority of your work (choose **one** option):

	✔
your line manager asks to you join her in an important meeting	✓
a colleague has too much work to do and wants you to help	
a colleague tells you that your computer screen will give you eye strain	
there is a fire drill and you have to temporarily evacuate the building	

✓

Task 10.3

Match the planning aid in the left-hand column with the appropriate type of activity in the right-hand column. Draw lines as appropriate.

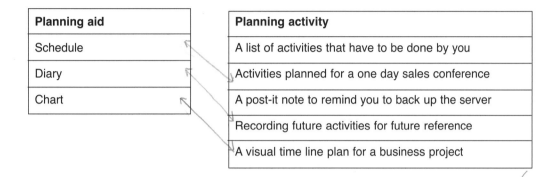

Planning aid
Schedule
Diary
Chart

Planning activity
A list of activities that have to be done by you
Activities planned for a one day sales conference
A post-it note to remind you to back up the server
Recording future activities for future reference
A visual time line plan for a business project

Task 10.4

Match the planning aid in the left-hand column with the appropriate type of activity in the right-hand column. Draw lines as appropriate.

Planning aid
'To do' list
Action plan
Wall planner

Planning activity
A list of activities that have to be done by you
Activities planned for a one day sales conference
A list of activities to be done by different people
Recording future activities for future reference
A visual time line plan for a business project

Task 10.5

You are a part-time Accounts Assistant employed by Froyd Limited, a printing business. Your main task is to process the payroll, but you also deal with checking incoming payments, preparing payments to suppliers and dealing with petty cash and the petty cash book.

Your working hours are 09.00 to 13.00 Monday to Friday.

You normally attend the weekly staff meeting at 11.00 every Wednesday.

Most employees are salaried and are paid monthly by direct bank transfer (BACS). Their salaries are processed on the last Wednesday of the month and reach their bank account on the last Friday of the month.

Some casual workers have chosen to be paid weekly by BACS and their salaries are processed every Wednesday and reach the bank account every Friday.

Other casual employees are still paid weekly in cash. The payroll for these employees is processed every Wednesday and paid every Friday. One of your jobs is to go to the bank on Thursday to pick up the cash to make up the pay packets for distribution on Friday. At the same time you also pick up from the bank the notes and coins needed to top up the petty cash.

Your normal routine during the week is set out on the schedule below.

Task description	Scheduling of tasks		Time taken
	Day	Time	for task
Process payments received	Monday	9.00	4 hours
Process payments made to suppliers and petty cash payments	Tuesday	9.00	4 hours
Process the payroll (BACS and cash)	Wednesday	9.00	3 hours
Update and balance the petty cash book	Thursday	9.00	2 hour
Visit bank to pick up cash wages and petty cash	Thursday	11.00	1 hour
Lock the cash in the safe and petty cash box	Thursday	12.00	1 hour
Make up cash pay packets and distribute payslips for all employees	Friday	9.00	3 hours

On the last Wednesday in July you and your car are involved in a minor road accident on the way to work. Nobody is hurt but the driver of the other car is not very cooperative and as a result you do not get into the office until 12.00.

The Accounts Manager is very sympathetic as you are a bit shaken up, but he points out that both the weekly and monthly payroll must meet their deadlines as all the staff will need paying on Friday. He suggests that you prioritise what you have to do for the rest of the week. He has agreed to let you work additional hours on Thursday afternoon so that you can ensure that all the tasks are completed.

(a) Using the table below, write a 'to do' list for the rest of Wednesday morning, Thursday and Friday by listing the tasks in order of completion. Write the task descriptions in the column on the right.

Choose from the following tasks:

Make up cash pay packets and distribute payslips for all employees

✓ Update and balance the petty cash book

~~Deal with payments made to suppliers and petty cash payments~~

✓ Process the payroll (BACS and cash)

✓ Lock the cash in the safe and petty cash box

✓ Visit the bank to pick up cash wages and petty cash top up

~~Process payments received~~

WEDNESDAY/THURSDAY/FRIDAY 'TO DO' LIST (in order of completion)	
Task 1	Process the payroll (BACs + cash) Wed -12-1 Thu - 9-11
Task 2	Update + balance petty cash book 11-1
Task 3	Visit bank to pick up wages + cash 1-2
Task 4	Lock cash v safe 2-3
Task 5	Make up cash packets

(b) If you **do not** carry out the instructions of the Accounts Manager there could be problems. Indicate below whether the following outcomes could have serious consequences for Froyd Ltd or not.

	serious	not serious
The staff may not get paid on time.	✓	
The cash from the bank may not get locked away.	✓	
Petty cash reimbursements may be delayed.		✓
Suppliers may not get paid on time.		✓
Minor office duties may not get done.		✓

11 Dealing with conflicts and dissatisfaction at work

Task 11.1

If you suspect that your line manager is showing favouritism to a colleague at your expense, you should (tick the appropriate option):

✔

talk to your colleague about the problem	
talk to a more senior manager about the problem when you have an appraisal	✓
take the matter to an Industrial Tribunal	

✓

Task 11.2

You see that a colleague is stealing small items of stationery such as paper, pens and staplers.

You should (tick the appropriate option):

✔

ask your colleague why she does it	
refer it to your line manager if it continues	✓
replace the items yourself	

✓

Task 11.3

You notice that a colleague is taking short cuts in her invoicing work and not following the normal checking processes set down in the procedures manual. As a result, mistakes are occurring and the whole team is getting the blame. The action you should take is as follows (tick the appropriate option):

✔

refer it straight to the Senior Accounts Manager	
talk to your colleague about it in the first instance, pointing out the errors	✓
amend the procedures manual	

Task 11.4

Your line manager (an older man) is constantly making sexist remarks to the whole office at the expense of a young female trainee – for example 'You can't expect her to get it right first time, she's had another blonde moment!'

She has expressed her concern by getting very upset and rushing off to the rest-room in tears, but the line manager takes no notice.

The appropiate action to be taken is (tick the correct option):

✔

the girl should pursue the matter through the Grievance Procedure	✓
you and your colleagues should organise a petition to the Managing Director	
the police should be called in as the Sex Discrimination Act is involved	

12 Continuing Professional Development

Task 12.1

The order of the main stages in the CPD (Continuing Professional Development) process is:

	✔
identification of objectives, identification of needs, identification of learning methods, evaluation of success	
identification of needs, identification of objectives, identification of learning methods, evaluation of success	✓
identification of needs, identification of learning methods, identification of objectives, evaluation of success	

Task 12.2

'SMART' objectives in the CPD (Continuing Professional Development) process are (tick the correct option):

	✔
Specific, Measurable, Achievable, Realistic, Timely	✓
Secure, Meaningful, Accurate, Realistic, Timely	
Safe, Measurable, Accurate, Realistic, Timely	

Task 12.3

Which of the following is **not** part of the normal CPD (Continuing Professional Development) process? Tick the appropriate option.

✔

Studying for a further qualification.	
Progressing to another job with the same employer.	
Changing to the same job with a different employer.	✓

✓

Task 12.4

Your manager has recently reviewed your performance and identified your strengths and weaknesses. He has suggested a number of ways in which you can improve your performance (remedying weaknesses) and develop your skills (developing your strengths).

You are to match the strength and the weakness on the left with the appropriate improvement and development opportunities on the right. Draw two lines as appropriate.

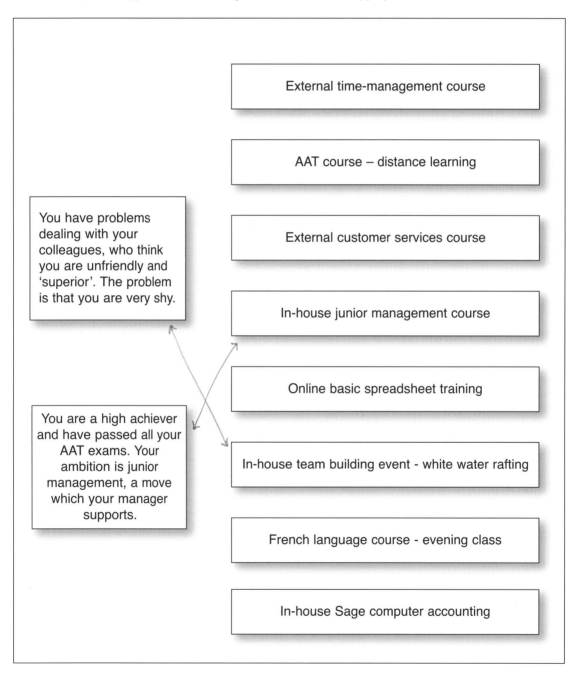

Work effectively in accounting

Practice activity answers

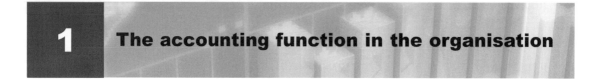

1   The accounting function in the organisation

Task 1.1

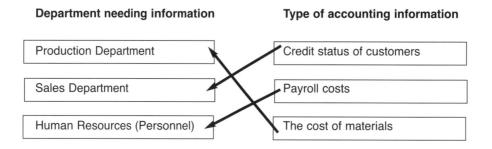

Department needing information	Type of accounting information
Production Department	Credit status of customers
Sales Department	Payroll costs
Human Resources (Personnel)	The cost of materials

Task 1.2

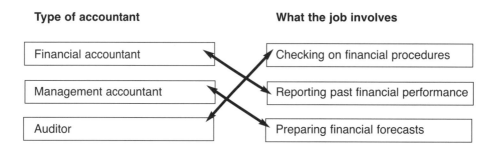

Type of accountant	What the job involves
Financial accountant	Checking on financial procedures
Management accountant	Reporting past financial performance
Auditor	Preparing financial forecasts

Task 1.3

calculating the cost of products	
recording production data such as hours worked	
preparing sales reports for management	✔
preparing production reports for management	

Task 1.4

recording customer orders, issuing invoices, receiving credit notes	
recording orders made by the business, receiving invoices, receiving credit notes	✔
recording orders made by the business, issuing invoices, receiving credit notes	
recording customer orders, issuing invoices, issuing credit notes	

Smooth running, solvency and legal compliance within an organisation

Task 2.1

	Improves smooth running ✔	Makes no difference ✔
A Disciplinary Procedures document	✔	
A 'green' policy of recycling paper		✔
A staff holiday plan to even out absences	✔	
A manual of accounting procedures	✔	
A weekly fire evacuation drill		✔

Task 2.2

	Solvency ✔	Legal compliance ✔
Paying employee income tax deductions to HMRC		✔
Avoiding having to pay overtime to employees	✔	
Making sure credit customers pay up on time	✔	
Completing the VAT Return for HMRC		✔
Completing the VAT Return on time to avoid a fine	✔	

Task 2.3

	smooth running ✔	improving solvency ✔	legal compliance ✔
Reporting on late payments to suppliers	✔		
Chasing up payments due by customers		✔	
Banking cheques payable to the business promptly		✔	
Carrying out a bank reconciliation statement	✔		
Insuring the company cars			✔
Paying the National Insurance Contributions of employees to HMRC			✔

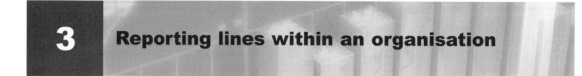

3   Reporting lines within an organisation

Task 3.1

Tommy Wong (Accounts Manager)	Finance Director
Anna Graniello (Chief Cashier)	Accounts Manager
David Schofield (Payroll Assistant)	Payroll Line Manager

Task 3.2

the Costing Manager only	
the Costing Manager and Production Manager only	
the Costing Manager and Production Manager and appropriate people in other departments of the business	✔

4 Policies and procedures within an organisation

Task 4.1

regulations imposed by law which must be adopted by an organisation	
regulations set up by an organisation which must be adopted by that organisation	✔
the terms relating to the sales of goods and services by an organisation	
a contract of employment issued by an organisation	

Task 4.2

grievance procedures for staff complaints	✔
environmental policy	
quality control in manufacture	
emergency procedures for suspected letter bomb	✔

5   Working with numbers

Task 5.1

(a)	29.4	29
(b)	29.5	30
(c)	29.6	30
(d)	29.612	30
(e)	29.498	30
(f)	29.436	29

Task 5.2

(a)	1.484	1.48
(b)	1.445	1.45
(c)	1.438	1.44
(d)	453.41233	453.41
(e)	453.41546	453.42
(f)	453.77612	453.78

Task 5.3

(a)   as a fraction of the class

$^2/_3$ (ie $^{12}/_{18}$)

(b)   a percentage of the class
rounded to the nearest number

67%

(c)   the ratio of females to males
in the class

2 : 3

Task 5.4

(a)   a fraction of the people invited

$^1/_4$

(b)   a percentage of the people invited

25%

(c)   the ratio of people who came
to those who stayed away

1 : 3

(d)   a fraction of those invited

$^3/_8$

(e)   a percentage (one decimal place)
of those invited

37.5%

(f)   the ratio of people who came
to those who stayed away

3 : 5

Task 5.5

	amount on receipt £	VAT amount £	net amount £
(a)	12.00	2.00	10.00
(b)	5.76	0.96	4.80
(c)	10.74	1.79	8.95

Task 5.6

(a)   £1,200.50 | £1,440.60 |

(b)   £456.24 | £547.48 |

(c)   £12.99 | £15.58 |

Task 5.7

	total amount £	VAT charged £	final invoice amount £
(a)	1,250.00	237.50	1487.50
(b)	495.20	94.08	589.28
(c)	845.60	160.66	1,006.26

Task 5.8 (a) to (d)

Sales Manager	Week 1 £	Week 2 £	Week 3 £	Week 4 £	Total £
Briggs	5,450	16,975	8,291	13,175	43,891
Lucas	9,632	12,197	3,046	12,316	37,191
Patel	8,705	10,114	9,277	11,207	39,303
Hartmann	7,812	12,093	10,630	12,951	43,486
Ponti	8,361	10,176	12,950	16,230	47,717
TOTALS	39,960	61,555	44,194	65,879	211,588

(e)

Sales Manager	Total sales £	5% Commission due work to nearest £
Briggs	43,891	2,195
Lucas	37,191	1,860
Patel	39,303	1,965
Hartmann	43,486	2,174
Ponti	47,717	2,386

(f)

	£
Original amount including VAT	37,191.00
Minus VAT content (amount x $\frac{1}{6}$)	6,198.50
Correct sales total for Lucas	30,992.50
Revised commission @ 5%	1,550.00

(g) The error amounts to £310.00

6 Communication skills – use of correct grammar

Task 6.1

Its time to study.	
It's time to study.	✔
I hate this pasta; I do not like it's taste.	
I hate this pasta; I do not like its taste.	✔

Task 6.2

It's been raining non-stop for two weeks.	✔
Its been raining non-stop for two weeks.	
I love this carpet; I really like it's colour.	
I love this carpet; I really like its colour.	✔

Task 6.3

Its been ages since I saw you.	
It's been ages since I saw you.	✔
I like this coffee; it's aroma is very strong.	
I like this coffee; its aroma is very strong.	✔

Task 6.4

I like your perfume, its scent reminds me of roses.	✔
I like your perfume, it's scent reminds me of roses.	
I am glad I met you; its been a great evening.	
I am glad I met you; it's been a great evening.	✔

Task 6.5

There are many textbooks available.	✔
Their are many textbooks available.	
They're are many textbooks available.	

Task 6.6

Have the students taken there assessments yet?	
Have the students taken they're assessments yet?	
Have the students taken their assessments yet?	✔

Task 6.7

The students are sure that there competent.	
The students are sure that they're competent.	✔
The students are sure that their competent.	

Task 6.8

It's there problem, not mine!	
It's they're problem, not mine!	
It's their problem, not mine!	✔

Task 6.9

This curry is far two hot for me!	
This curry is far too hot for me!	✔
This curry is far to hot for me!	

Task 6.10

These questions make me go two sleep.	
These questions make me go too sleep.	
These questions make me go to sleep.	✔

Task 6.11

Two much double-entry is bad for your health.	
Too much double-entry is bad for your health.	✔
To much double-entry is bad for your health.	

Task 6.12

Two is company, three is a crowd.	✔
Too is company, three is a crowd.	
To is company, three is a crowd.	

7 Communication skills – letters and emails

Task 7.1

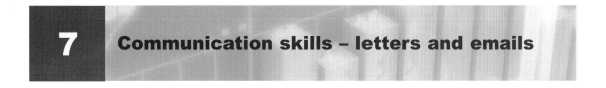

From   c.brooks@gerrardsportsgoods.com

To   a.banerjee@gerrardsportsgoods.com

Subject   Manufacturing data for July **1**

Hi Ayan

Please send me the quantity of 'Anfield' footballs **2** manufactured

during the month of   July   **3** . We need this information to carry

out a costing exercise. I need the information, please, by 2 August **4** .

Many thanks and kind regards

Charlie

Accounts Department

Task 7.2

incorrect word	correction
Miss	Mrs
recomend	recommend
seperate	separate
Their	They're – or, better – They are
faithfully	sincerely

8 Report writing – report structure

Task 8.1

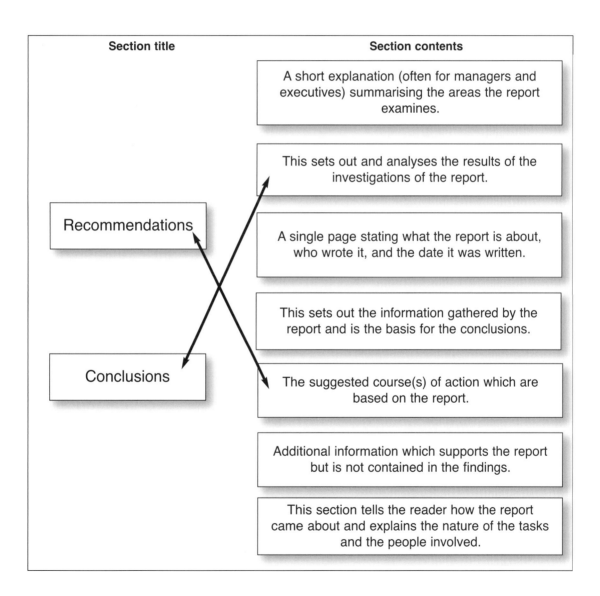

Section title	Section contents
	A short explanation (often for managers and executives) summarising the areas the report examines.
	This sets out and analyses the results of the investigations of the report.
Recommendations	A single page stating what the report is about, who wrote it, and the date it was written.
	This sets out the information gathered by the report and is the basis for the conclusions.
Conclusions	The suggested course(s) of action which are based on the report.
	Additional information which supports the report but is not contained in the findings.
	This section tells the reader how the report came about and explains the nature of the tasks and the people involved.

9   Report writing – report contents

Task 9.1

(a)

RESULTS OF STAFF CPD QUESTIONNAIRE			
Question	**Good %**	**Fair %**	**Poor %**
How do you rate your motivation for doing your current job?	14	46	40
How do you rate the training you are given in your job?	8	44	48
How do you rate your opportunities for promotion?	6	54	40

(b)

The results for motivation and promotion opportunities were both excellent.	
The result for motivation was less positive than the result for promotion opportunites.	
The worst result related to the quality of staff training.	✔
There is no real reason for changing the present training system.	
All areas of CPD (motivation, training and promotion) need urgent attention.	✔
Staff seem very happy with the present system of training and promotion.	

(c)

Reduce the number of staff so that there will be more opportunity for individuals to go on training courses.	
Review and expand the training programmes so that there is more opportunity for improving staff performance and motivation.	✔
Schedule and carry out CPD interviews with all members of staff so that individual needs are fulfilled and motivation improved.	✔
Reduce the frequency of staff interviews so that they will have less opportunity to complain and get demoralised.	

10 Managing the workload, scheduling and the effects of non-completion

10.1

tell your line manager	✔
not tell your line manager	
tell a colleague that he/she should help you	
say you have a bad headache and you need to go home	

10.2

your line manager asks to you join her in an important meeting	✔
a colleague has too much work to do and wants you to help	
a colleague tells you that your computer screen will give you eye strain	
there is a fire drill and you have to temporarily evacuate the building	

Task 10.3

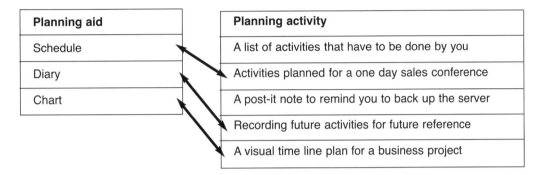

Planning aid	Planning activity
Schedule	A list of activities that have to be done by you
Diary	Activities planned for a one day sales conference
Chart	A post-it note to remind you to back up the server
	Recording future activities for future reference
	A visual time line plan for a business project

Task 10.4

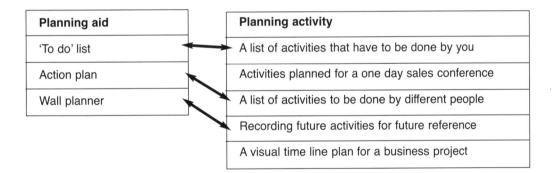

Planning aid	Planning activity
'To do' list	A list of activities that have to be done by you
Action plan	Activities planned for a one day sales conference
Wall planner	A list of activities to be done by different people
	Recording future activities for future reference
	A visual time line plan for a business project

Task 10.5 (a)

WEDNESDAY/THURSDAY/FRIDAY 'TO DO' LIST (in order of completion)	
Task 1	Process the payroll (BACS and cash)
Task 2	Update and balance the petty cash book
Task 3	Visit the bank to pick up cash wages and petty cash top up
Task 4	Lock the cash in the safe at work
Task 5	Make up cash pay packets and distribute payslips for all employees

(b)

	serious	not serious
The staff may not get paid on time.	✔	
The cash from the bank may not get locked away.	✔	
Petty cash reimbursements may be delayed.		✔
Suppliers may not get paid on time.	✔	
Minor office duties may not get done.		✔

11 Dealing with conflicts and dissatisfaction at work

Task 11.1

talk to your colleague about the problem	
talk to a more senior manager about the problem when you have an appraisal	✔
take the matter to an Industrial Tribunal	

Task 11.2

ask your colleague why she does it	
refer it to your line manager if it continues	✔
replace the items yourself	

Task 11.3

refer it straight to the Senior Accounts Manager	
talk to your colleague about it in the first instance, pointing out the errors	✔
amend the procedures manual	

Task 11.4

the girl should pursue the matter through the Grievance Procedure	✔
you and your colleagues should organise a petition to the Managing Director	
the police should be called in as the Sex Discrimination Act is involved	

12 Continuing Professional Development

Task 12.1

identification of objectives, identification of needs, identification of learning methods, evaluation of success	
identification of needs, identification of objectives, identification of learning methods, evaluation of success	✔
identification of needs, identification of learning methods, identification of objectives, evaluation of success	

Task 12.2

Specific, Measurable, Achievable, Realistic, Timely	✔
Secure, Meaningful, Accurate, Realistic, Timely	
Safe, Measurable, Accurate, Realistic, Timely	

Task 12.3

Studying for a further qualification.	
Progressing to another job with the same employer.	
Changing to the same job with a different employer.	✔

Task 12.4

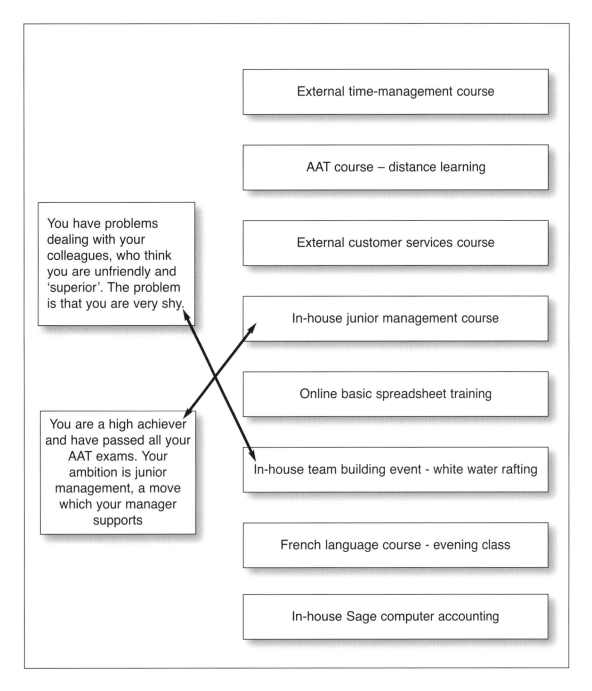

Work effectively in accounting

Practice assessment 1

Task 1

(a)   Which **two** of the following policies and procedures are most likely to be relevant to the accounting function?

	✔
Emergency procedures for fire	✓
Disciplinary procedures	✓
Clothing worn on the production line	
The use of environmentally friendly cleaning materials	

(b)   Which **two** of the following options are external stakeholders to which a business is likely to provide accounting information? Tick the appropriate options.

	✔
The Production Department	
The tax authorities	✓
Its competitors	
The bank	✓

(c)   Accounting information provided should be (choose **one** option):

	✔	
Complete, mostly accurate and produced as quickly as possible		
Complete, accurate and on time		✓
Mostly complete, accurate and on time	✓	+

Task 2

(a) Indicate with a tick in the appropriate column below which aspect of running a business best describes the activities listed in the left-hand column. Choose from:

(a) ensuring the smooth running of a business

(b) improving the solvency of a business

(c) compliance with legal requirements by the business

	smooth running ✔	improving solvency ✔	legal compliance ✔
Processing the payroll in good time	✓		
Sending out customer statements on time		✓	
Sending out payment to suppliers at the latest possible date		✓	
Complying with Health & Safety regulations			✓
Ensuring that there is no sex discrimination at work			✓
Keeping the filing up-to-date	✓		

(b) 'Solvency' can best be defined as (choose **one** option):

	✔
The balance of money in the bank account	
Being able to pay debts when they are due	✓
Keeping up to date with paying suppliers	
Obtaining the best return on money invested for the long term	

(c) 'Working capital' of a business is best defined as (choose **one** option):

	✔
Share capital of a company owned by its employees	
The balance of money kept in a bank account	
Day-to-day funds available to a business	✓
Money due from customers plus money due to suppliers	

(d) Areas of work such as the Accounting Department are subject to legislation. Some situations within a department are covered by specific laws (legislation), some are not.

In the left-hand column of the table set out below are a number of situations. You are to enter in the right-hand column the name of the area of legislation which applies, or if there is no law applicable, enter 'not applicable'. The choice of legislation which might apply is:

Health & Safety at Work   Data Protection

situation	area of legislation, or 'not applicable'
Eyestrain experienced by a computer operator	H + S
An employee with very bad breath which annoys other people in the workplace	N/A
An employee who provides his address to the employer's Human Resources Department for internal use	Data protection N/A ✗
An employee who provides the address of a customer to another business	Data protection
An employee accidentally washes her hands in bleach in the staff kitchen and burns her hands	H+S
An employee cycling to work accidentally runs into a pedestrian who is then injured	N/A
An employee receives a telephone call from a local radio station wanting the name and address of an employee who has won a prize in a competition	Data protection

Task 3

Your name is Sam and you work as an assistant in the payroll section of Crocus Limited and have been passed the draft email (shown below) to complete.

The email is a request to Nishit Thacker (nthacker@crocus.co.uk), an assistant in the Human Resources Department, to provide details of hours worked in March by all the employees of the company, listed by department. You need the information by 5 April.

You are to:

(a)   Insert the email address of the recipient in the appropriate box.

(b)   Complete the remaining boxes (they are numbered for reference) with the most appropriate words or phrases from the lists shown below (also numbered for reference).

From	sam.sung@crocus.co.uk
To	*nthacker@crocw.co.uk*
Subject	*March hours worked + March payroll data* **1**

Hi Nishit

Please send me the hours worked by   *all employees by dept.*   **2**

for the month of   *March*   **3**. It would be useful if you could send

me this data on the usual spreadsheet. I need the information by   *5 April*   **4**.

Many thanks and kind regards

Sam

Payroll, Accounts Department

Option Lists

Pick one word or phrase for each numbered box from the following numbered lists:

1   Payroll, Hours by department, March payroll data, March hours worked

2   employees in the Accounts Department, all employees, all employees by department

3   March, April, May, June

4   5 March, 15 March, 5 April, 15 April

Task 4

You are an Accounts Assistant employed by Hokkni Limited. You work mostly on the Sales Ledger section.

Your working hours are 09.00 to 17.00 with an hour for lunch from 13.00 to 14.00.

You have a staff meeting every Tuesday at 11.00 which is compulsory.

Your other duties during the week are set out on the schedule below.

Task description	Scheduling of tasks		Time taken
	Day	Time	for task
Dealing with emails and the post	Daily	9.00	1 hour
Processing sales orders	Daily	10.00	1 hour
Processing payments by customers	Monday	14.00	2 hours
Sales invoicing and credit notes on Sage	Wednesday	14.00	2 hours
Updating the office filing	Thursday	11.00	1 hour
Preparing and sending out customer statements	Thursday	14.00	2 hours
Sending out overdue account letters	Friday	14.00	2 hours

On Wednesday, just as you are about to start to input a large pile of sales invoices on the computer, the main server crashes and all the computers in the office are put out of action. As you cannot input the invoices you carry on with some general filing work and other small jobs that need to be done.

Meanwhile the IT people are called in and the problem is eventually fixed at 4.45 pm.

The Accounts Manager then calls a short meeting for the Accounts Department staff and says:

"Sorry about the computer problem. It is all fixed now and you should be fine to carry on as normal tomorrow morning. I don't see the need to work any overtime now as I am sure you can catch up with your work then.

Please make sure that you carry out your normal routines as usual, in other words tasks like opening the post, answering emails and order processing; these need to be done and got out of the way first.

Lastly, this week is the last week of the month. It is critical that all the customer invoices and credit notes are input and printed, and the ledgers updated. We can then produce statements as usual tomorrow afternoon and send out overdue account letters on Friday."

(a)   Write a 'to do' list for Thursday set out below by listing the tasks in order of completion. Write the task descriptions in the column on the right.

Choose from the following tasks:

✓ Dealing with emails and the post

~~Processing payments by customers~~

✓ Processing sales orders

✓ Sending out overdue account letters

~~Updating the office filing~~

✓ Preparing and sending out customer statements

✓ Sales invoicing and credit notes on Sage

THURSDAY 'TO DO' LIST (in order of completion)	
Task 1	Dealing with emails + post
Task 2	Processing sales orders
Task 3	Sales invoicing + credit notes on Sage
Task 4	Preparing + sending out customer statements.
Task 5	Send out overdue account letts ✗ Friday!!

Update office filing

(b)   If you **do not carry out the instructions** of the Accounts Manager there could be problems. Tick the three likely outcomes that would occur if you **did not** reorganise your priority of tasks.

	✔
If statements or chaser letters are sent out late this would adversely affect the cash flow of the business.	✓
Processing of payments received from customers would be delayed. ✗	
The overdue account letters might not be produced on time.	✓
The office filing might be delayed.	
The post may not get opened.	
The statements might not be produced on time.	✓

Task 5

You have been passed the following draft letter (to a Mr Joliewski) to check.

There are five major errors which could include wrong spellings, bad grammar or the wrong use of words.

You are to:

(a)   Identify the five incorrect words and enter them in the left-hand column of the table below.

(b)   Enter your correction of these five words on the appropriate line in the right-hand column of the table below.

Dear Mr Jeliowski,

Overdue invoice 27363

Please find inclosed a copy of invoice 27363 what you requested.

Please note that we have not yet recieved payment of this invoice to date and would be grateful if you will settle it within seven days.

If we do not receive the payment within this period we will have no alternative but to place the matter in the hands of our solicitor.

Yours faithfully,

---

incorrect word	correction
what	which
recieved	received
Jeliowski	Joliewski
inclosed	enclosed
yours faithfully	yours sincerely

Task 6

Atlas Limited is a UK company which divides its sales force into four regions. The provisional sales figures for the last three months are shown below.

Region	Sales (£) January- March
South	456,400
West	349,340
North	410,520
East	274,840

-100100   30·61%

+ 100100

You have been asked to do some analysis of these figures and to carry out the tasks that follow.

(a) What are the total UK sales for January to March?

1,491,100

(b) What percentage of total sales was made by the North Region? Round your answer to two decimal places.

27·53%

(c) What percentage of total sales was made by the South Region and the West Region combined? Round your answer to two decimal places.

54·04 %

(d) What percentage of total sales was made by the East Region? Round your answer to two decimal places.

18·43%

Your manager then tells you that there is a mistake in the way the figures have been compiled and says that £100,000 of sales have been allocated to the South Region which should have been allocated to the East Region.

(e) Calculate the revised sales figures in the table which follows by adjusting the sales figures for the South Region and the East Region by the amount of the error.

(f) Enter the total of the four Regions' sales in the total box.

Region	Revised Sales (£) January- March
South	356, 400
West	349, 340
North	410, 520
East	374, 840
Total sales	1, 491, 100

(g) What is the **revised** percentage of total sales made by the South Region?
Round your answer to two decimal places.

23.90 %

(h) What is the **revised** percentage of total sales made by the East Region?
Round your answer to two decimal places.

25.14 %

(i) Now answer the following question by ticking the appropriate option:

✔

The sales percentages of the South and East regions have not changed.	
The sales percentages of the South and East regions have both increased.	
The sales percentage of the South region has decreased and the sales percentage of the East region has increased.	✓
The sales percentage of the East region has decreased and the sales percentage of the South region has increased.	

Task 7

Your manager has recently reviewed your performance and identified your strengths and weaknesses. She has suggested a number of ways in which you can improve your performance (remedying weaknesses) and develop your skills (developing your strengths).

You are to match the strength and the weakness on the left with the appropriate improvement and development opportunities on the right. Draw two lines as appropriate.

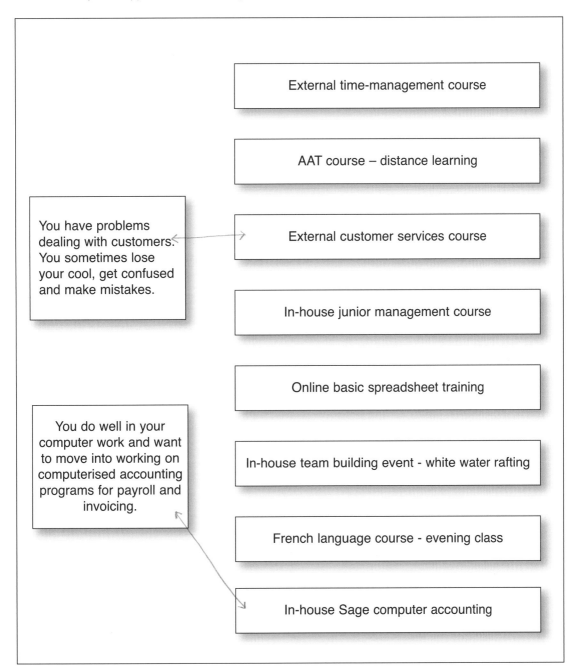

Task 8

(a)   A business report normally contains seven sections, each with a distinct function. The seven sections are:

1   Title

2   Summary

3   Introduction

4   Findings

5   Conclusions

6   Recommendations

7   Appendices

You are to match the two sections on the left with the appropriate descriptions on the right. Draw two lines as appropriate.

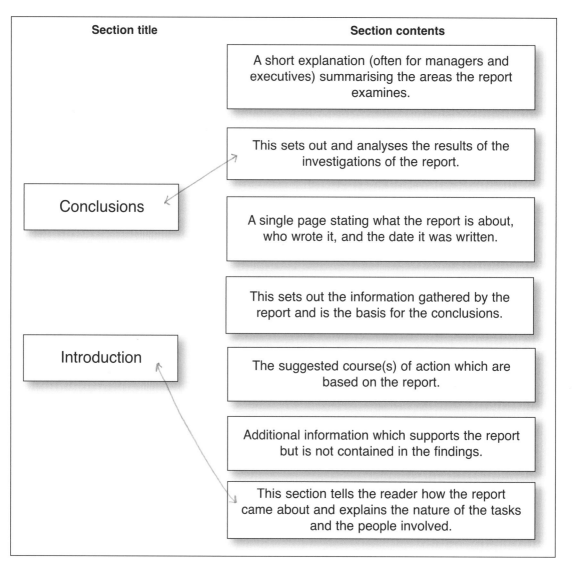

Section title	Section contents
	A short explanation (often for managers and executives) summarising the areas the report examines.
	This sets out and analyses the results of the investigations of the report.
Conclusions	A single page stating what the report is about, who wrote it, and the date it was written.
	This sets out the information gathered by the report and is the basis for the conclusions.
Introduction	The suggested course(s) of action which are based on the report.
	Additional information which supports the report but is not contained in the findings.
	This section tells the reader how the report came about and explains the nature of the tasks and the people involved.

Task 8

(b)   Pentola Limited is an old-fashioned manufacturing company. Many of its accounting systems are manual, although it has recently set up a computerised system which operates the ledgers. The Accounts Manager has been asked to produce a Report based on the investigation of the current payroll system which is totally paper-based and expensive to operate. Her main task is to reduce costs in the business.

You are a Costing Assistant and have been asked to investigate the annual costs of **three options** and see how they work out over a three year period, and decide which is the least expensive.

Option 1   the existing manual system as it stands, which is very labour-intensive

Option 2   the possibility of computerising the system, which will need updated computer equipment and require staff training

Option 3   paying an external payroll bureau to process the payroll

Your findings, which will be incorporated in the Report, are as follows:

	Annual running cost (£)	Set-up costs (£)
Manual payroll system (in-house)	4,000	None
Computerised payroll (in-house)	1,200	7,500
Payroll bureau (external)	5,000	None

You have been asked to:

1   calculate the **total cost for 3 years** (ie annual costs plus any set-up costs) for each option

2   calculate the **average cost per year** of each option (ie total cost divided by 3)

Use the table below to make your calculations.

PENTOLA LIMITED – 3 YEAR PAYROLL COST AND AVERAGE COST PER YEAR				
Payroll system used	Total annual running cost (3 x annual running cost) £	Set-up cost £	Total cost for 3 years £	Average annual cost £
Manual payroll (in-house)	12,000	0.00	12,000	4000
Computerised payroll (in-house)	3,600	7,500.00	11,100	3700
Payroll bureau (external)	15,000	0.00	15,000	5,000

Now complete Tasks 8(c) and 8(d) which follow.

(c) Select **TWO conclusions** to be included in the Report. The conclusions should be based on the **cost** of the three options calculated in Task 8(b). Tick the appropriate boxes.

✔

The existing manual payroll system is the cheapest option over the three years.	
The computerised payroll system is the cheapest option over the three years.	✓
It would be better and cheaper in the long run to have the payroll processed by an external payroll bureau.	
It would not be a good idea to use the computerised payroll option because the set-up costs are so high.	
It would be a good idea to use the computerised payroll option because the set-up costs are only a 'one-off' expense and the long-term total costs are lower.	✓
It would be a good idea to use the external payroll bureau because it would reduce the need for staff training.	

(d) Select **TWO recommendations** to be included in the Report and based on the conclusions in (c) above. Tick the appropriate boxes.

✔

Call a meeting of Accounts staff who work on payroll and tell them that they will be expected to work more efficiently when using the manual system.	
Call a meeting of Accounts staff and explain to them the benefits using a computerised accounting system and promise them suitable training.	✓
Call a staff meeting and tell the employees that the payroll will be processed by an external bureau.	
Draw up a plan for the extra computer equipment that will be needed and obtain further information about computer accounting training courses.	✓

Task 9

(a) A Line Manager in charge of the Purchase Ledger section of an Accounting Department will **normally** be reported to by (indicate the correct option):

✔

Purchase Ledger Assistants only	✓
Assistants in the Accounting Department only	
Assistants from a variety of Departments	

+ ✓

(b) A Line Manager in charge of the Payroll section of an Accounting Department will **normally** be reported to by (indicate the correct option):

✔

Payroll Assistants only	✓
Payroll and other Assistants	
the Accounts Manager	

✓

+

(c)

A cashier finds she has made a major error in the Cash Book which means that the business could go overdrawn at the bank. She should:

✔

Keep quiet and hope that the error will not be noticed	
Report the problem direct to the Finance Director	
Report the problem to her Line Manager	✓

(d) Problems and conflicts at work will need to be resolved. Sometimes they can be sorted out personally with an individual, sometimes they will need to be referred to a line manager. Assume that you are an Accounts Assistant and indicate below which issues can be resolved by you, and which will need to be referred to a line manager.

	by you	by a manager
A colleague keeps taking your crisps	✓	
A colleague keeps taking office postage stamps		✓
A colleague has bad body odour		✓

Work effectively in accounting

Practice assessment 2

Task 1

(a) An employee code of conduct is normally observed by members of an accounting department. Which **one** of the following is **not** normally covered by a code of conduct?

	✔
Working under the influence of alcohol or drugs	
Applying the correct VAT rate to an invoice	✓
Using a work computer to access pornographic material	
Using a work computer to send private emails	

(b) A stakeholder of a business is likely to be interested in accounting information. Match the stakeholder in the left-hand column with the most appropriate accounting information in the right-hand column.

Stakeholder
HM Revenue & Customs
Bank
Suppliers

Accounting information
Cash available to repay loans
Checking supplier invoices
VAT figures
Credit record for payment of trade debts
Payroll calculations
Petty cash book

(c) Sales order processing involves the following tasks (choose **one** option):

	✔
Recording orders received, producing invoices, producing credit notes	✓
Recording orders made, receiving invoices, checking credit notes	
Checking orders received, producing invoices, checking payments received	

Task 2

(a)   Indicate with a tick in the appropriate column below which aspect of running a business best describes the activities listed in the left-hand column. Choose from:

(a)   ensuring the smooth running of a business

(b)   improving the solvency of a business

(c)   compliance with legal requirements by the business

	smooth running ✔	improving solvency ✔	legal compliance ✔
Paying supplier invoices by the due date	✓		
Negotiating a longer payment period from suppliers		✓	
Avoiding fines by sending tax information promptly to HMRC		✓	
Sending the employer annual payroll return to HMRC			✓
Backing up computer files containing personal data	✓		
Keeping computer files containing personal data confidential			✓

(b)   Solvency can be achieved by careful management of money and liquidity. State whether or not the following actions help improve solvency. Tick the appropriate box.

	yes ✔	no ✔
Chasing up overdue customer accounts	✓	
Giving customers longer credit periods		✓
Paying suppliers as soon as possible		✓
Paying suppliers as late as possible	✓	

(c) The cash flow of a business can be positive or negative (ie money can come in, or come out), depending on the transaction. Identify which of the following cash flows are positive or negative.

	positive ✔	negative ✔
An increase in the average payment period given to credit customers		✓
An increase in the average payment period given by suppliers	✓	
A business pays cheques received into the bank every day	✓	
A business increases its trade discounts to its customers		✓

(d) An employer that requires its delivery van drivers to work 12 hour shifts with only six hours break between the shifts is in breach of (choose **one** option):

	✔
Health & Safety at Work legislation	
The Highway Code	
Working Time Regulations	✓

Task 3

Your name is Riley Morgan and you work as an assistant in the Accounts Department of Delphian Software and have been passed the draft email (shown below) to complete.

The email is a request to Ranveer Singh (rsingh@delphiansoftware.co.uk), Manager of the Sales and Marketing Department to attend a meeting to discuss improving the credit control of the company's customers. The meeting is at 11.30 on 13 July and will be held in the No. 2 Conference Room.

You are to:

(a)   Insert the email address of the recipient in the appropriate box.

(b)   Complete the remaining boxes (they are numbered for reference) with the most appropriate words or phrases from the lists shown below (also numbered for reference).

From   rmorgan@delphiansoftware.co.uk

To   *rsingh@delphiansoftware.co.uk*

Subject   *Credit control meeting*   [1]

Hello Ranveer

We are holding a meeting to discuss   *credit control systems*   [2]

on   *13th July at 11.30*   [3]   . This meeting will be held in the

No 2 conference room   [4]   . It would be very helpul if you could attend.

Many thanks and kind regards

Riley Morgan

Accounts Department

Option Lists

Pick one phrase for each numbered box from the following numbered lists:

[1]   purchase control meeting, sales meeting, sales figures meeting, credit control meeting

[2]   sales ledger systems, credit control systems, sales policy, product pricing

[3]   13 June at 11.30, 13 June, 13 July at 11.00, 13 July at 11.30

[4]   No. 1 Conference Room, No. 2 Committee Room, No. 2 Conference Room

Task 4

You are an Accounts Assistant employed by Miller Limited. You carry out a wide variety of tasks.

Your working hours are 09.00 to 17.00 with an hour for lunch from 13.00 to 14.00. Staff do not normally work overtime as a matter of policy, except if the situation is absolutely critical.

You have a staff meeting every Friday at 11.00 which is compulsory.

Your other duties during the week are set out on the schedule below.

Task description	Scheduling of tasks		Time taken
	Day	**Time**	**for task**
Dealing with emails and the post	Daily	9.00	1 hour
Processing sales invoices	Daily	10.00	1 hour
Processing payments to suppliers	Tuesday	11.00	2 hours
Credit control - sending chasers	Wednesday	15.00	2 hours
Processing the payroll	Thursday	15.00	2 hours
Listing the cheques and cash for paying in at the bank	Friday	12.00	1 hour
Paying in at the bank	Friday	14.00	1 hour

One Thursday afternoon just as you are leaving the office you receive the following email from the Accounts Manager:

Hi Alex

friday

I am having a meeting here at 12.00 tomorrow with John Lucas, Finance Director of Gerda Construction Ltd.

Can you let me have all the latest sales figures, credit limit and account history on my desk by 11.00 on Friday latest, please.

Sorry about the short notice.

Thanks

(a)   The Manager's request will obviously put you under pressure, but you should be able to do the job if you prioritise your tasks carefully. Consider the ways in which you should deal with the Manager's request for the figures for Friday's meeting and tick the option below which you think is the most appropriate.

✔

Email to say that your work schedule will not allow you to do the task in time.	
Reply to say that you will have the figures for him if you can do overtime on Thursday evening.	
Confirm that you will have the figures for him in time for his meeting on Friday.	✓
Do not reply to him but just hope that you can provide the figures in time.	

(b)   Complete the 'to do' list for Friday set out below by listing the tasks in order of completion. Write the task descriptions in the column on the right.

Choose from the following tasks:

Dealing with emails and the post

Processing sales invoices

Processing payments to suppliers

Credit control - sending chasers

Processing the payroll

Listing the cheques and cash for paying in at the bank

Paying in at the bank

Preparing account information for Gerda Construction Ltd

FRIDAY 'TO DO' LIST (in order of completion)	
Task 1	preparing a/c info for Gerda 9. 11
Task 2	dealing with emails + post 11-12
Task 3	processing sales invoices 12-1
Task 4	listing cheques + cash paying in at bank -
Task 5	paying in at bank

Task 5

You have been passed the following draft letter (to a Mr Gibson) to check.

There are five major errors which could include wrong spellings, bad grammar or the wrong use of words.

You are to:

(a) Identify the five incorrect words and enter them in the left-hand column of the table below.

(b) Enter your correction of these five words on the appropriate line in the right-hand column of the table below.

Dear Mr Gibson,

<u>Extenson of credit limit to £50,000</u>

Thank you 4 your letter of 23 March asking for an increase in your credit limit to £50,000.

We are pleased to advice you that we are happy to agree to this request and have carried out all the neccesary ammendments to our records.

Yours sincerely,

---

incorrect word	correction
extenson	extension
4	for
advice	advise
neccesary	necessary
ammendments	amendments

Task 6

Mazota is a Korean car manufacturer which has a factory in Milton Keynes. It produces four models:

- the Whizz (a 2 wheel drive town car)
- the Fourlander (a 4 wheel drive car)
- the Sportstar (a 2 wheel drive sports car)
- the Rugged (a 4 wheel drive car)

Workers on each of the production lines compete to be as efficient as possible. The workers on the production line that produces the most cars receive a productivity pay bonus of 10% every three months. The amount paid is based on the average monthly pay of production workers.

The number of cars produced in the three month period of April to June was as follows:

Vehicle	Cars produced April - June
Whizz	15,500
Fourlander (4 wheel drive)	24,760
Sportstar	18,300
Rugged (4 wheel drive)	11,840

(handwritten annotations: — 33,800   36,600)

You have been asked to do some analysis of these figures and to carry out the tasks that follow.

(a) What is the total number of cars produced from April to June?

70,400 ✓

(b) What percentage of total cars produced was made on the Whizz production line? Round your answer to the nearest whole figure.

22% ✓

(c) What percentage of total cars produced was made on the two 4 wheel drive cars production lines? Add the two production line figures together. Round your answer to the nearest whole figure.

52% ✓

(d) What percentage of total cars produced was made on the Sportstar production line? Round your answer to the nearest whole figure.

26% ✓

(e) The production line that qualifies for the 10% productivity bonus is the (tick the correct option):

	✔
Whizz	
Fourlander	✓
Sportstar	
Rugged	

(f) The average monthly pay of the Mazota production workers is £1,450. The workers that received the productivity bonus in June of 10% would receive in total (tick the correct amount):

	✔
£1,450 each	
£1,305 each	
£1,595 each	✓

(g) The number of 4 wheel drive cars produced by Mazota in April to June was (tick the correct option):

	✔
Less than the number of Sportstars produced in the same period	
Less than the number of Whizzes produced in the same period	
The same as the total of Sportstars and Whizzes added together	
Greater than the total of Sportstars and Whizzes added together	✓

✓

Task 7

Your manager has recently reviewed your performance and identified your strengths and weaknesses. He has suggested a number of ways in which you can improve your performance (remedying weaknesses) and develop your skills (developing your strengths).

You are to match the strength and the weakness on the left with the appropriate improvement and development opportunities on the right. Draw two lines as appropriate..

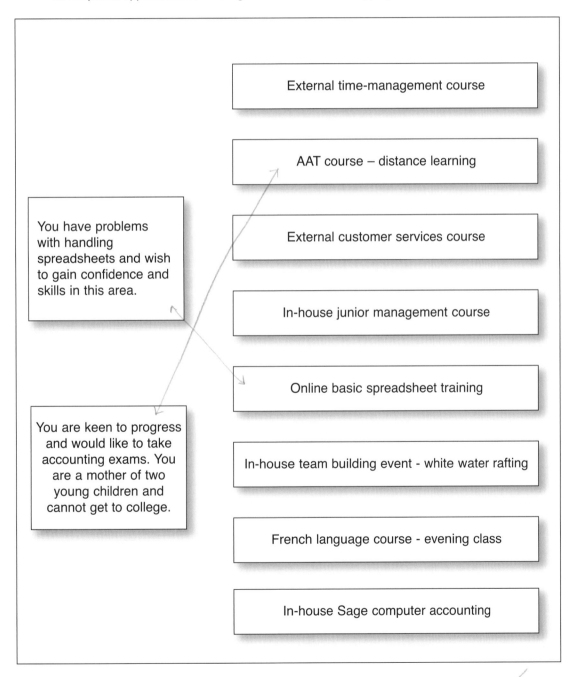

Task 8

(a) A business report normally contains seven sections, each with a distinct function. The seven sections are:

1 Title
2 Summary
3 Introduction
4 Findings
5 Conclusions
6 Recommendations
7 Appendices

You are to match the two sections on the left with the appropriate descriptions on the right. Draw two lines as appropriate.

Section title	Section contents
Summay	A short explanation (often for managers and executives) summarising the areas the report examines.
conclusions	This sets out and analyses the results of the investigations of the report.
Recommendations	A single page stating what the report is about, who wrote it, and the date it was written. *title*
	This sets out the information gathered by the report and is the basis for the conclusions.
Findings	The suggested course(s) of action which are based on the report.
appendices	Additional information which supports the report but is not contained in the findings.
Introducti	This section tells the reader how the report came about and explains the nature of the tasks and the people involved.

Task 8

(b)   There have been a number of customer complaints passed to the Accounts Manager of Nappho Limited about the level of customer service provided by the Accounts Department. The Accounts Manager therefore asked for a Report to be drafted following an online survey emailed to a sample of 55 customers.

The results of the survey are set out in the table below. A total of 25 replies were received from customers.

The areas being investigated were graded in three levels: 'Good', Satisfactory' and 'Unsatisfactory'.

RESULTS OF CUSTOMER SERVICE QUESTIONNAIRE (ACCOUNTS DEPARTMENT)			
Question	**Good**	**Satisfactory**	**Unsatisfactory**
How do you rate our customer service for politeness and readiness to help?	20	4	1
How well informed about our services and systems are the staff that you speak to?	12	7	6
How easy is it to get through the main switchboard to the Accounts Department?	5	8	12

Convert the figures in the above table to percentages of the total number of responses and complete the table below. Remember that there were 25 responses received.

RESULTS OF CUSTOMER SERVICE QUESTIONNAIRE (ACCOUNTS DEPARTMENT)			
Question	**Good** **%**	**Satisfactory** **%**	**Unsatisfactory** **%**
How do you rate our customer service for politeness and readiness to help?	80%	16%	4%
How well informed about our services and systems are the staff that you speak to?	48%	28%	24%
How easy is it to get through the main switchboard to the Accounts Department?	20%	32%	48%

Now complete Tasks 8(c) and 8(d) which follow.

(c) Select **THREE conclusions** to be included in the Report. Tick the appropriate boxes.

	✔
The results for customer service for politeness were good.	✓
The politeness of staff was thought to be generally less than satisfactory.	
Staff knowledge of service and systems was without fault.	
Staff knowledge of service and systems was at fault in a number of instances.	✓
The switchboard worked perfectly for all the customers.	
Many customers found it difficult in getting through the main switchboard to the Accounts Department.	✓

✓

(d) Select **TWO recommendations** to be included in the Report. Tick the appropriate boxes.

	✔
Take no action immediately but send out the questionnaire to another group of customers after six months.	
Timetable training sessions for Accounts staff in order to improve their technical knowledge, and suggest they enrol for an AAT course.	✓
Consult with the managerial staff in charge of the main company switchboard and ask that urgent action be taken to improve the service provided to customers.	✓
Suggest that customers are encouraged to send in emails rather than use the telephone to contact the Accounts Department staff.	

✓

Task 9

(a)   The person in an Accounts Department most likely to report to the Managing Director is:

	✔
Finance Director	✓
Sales Director	
Financial Accountant	
Payroll Manager	

(b)

The person in an Accounts Department most likely to oversee a Sales Ledger Assistant is:

	✔
Sales Manager	
Purchase Ledger Supervisor	
Accounts Manager	✓
Cashier	

(c) Problems and conflicts at work will need to be resolved. Sometimes they can be sorted out personally with an individual, sometimes they will need to be referred to a line manager. Assume that you are an Accounts Assistant and indicate below which issues can be resolved by you, and which will need to be referred to a line manager.

	by you	by manager
A colleague has a habit of asking you to finish the invoicing when she has to go to meet her boyfriend.	✓	
Your line manager assumes you are trained in spreadsheets but you are not and you have problems in trying to use them.		✓
A colleague is consistently making mistakes which reflects badly on your own work.		✓

Work effectively in accounting

Practice assessment 3

Task 1

(a) Which **one** of the following is **not** normally covered by the Policies and Procedures Manual of an accounting department?

	✔
Authorisation limits for the signing of cheques	
Authorisation limits for ordering goods and services	
Setting the tax codes issued for calculating employees' pay	✓
Operation of the petty cash system	

✓

(b) Match the accounting function in the left-hand column with the appropriate accounting activity in the right-hand column. Draw lines as appropriate.

Accounting function
Purchasing
Sales order processing
Costing

Accounting activity
Preparing a VAT return
Checking supplier invoices
Maintaining a cash book
Issuing invoices
Preparing budget reports
Payroll calculations

✓

(c) The accounting information needed by a payroll department includes which **two** of the following options? Tick the appropriate option

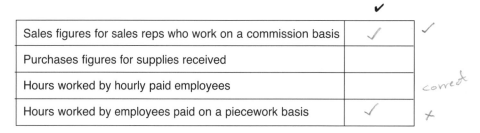

	✔	
Sales figures for sales reps who work on a commission basis	✓	✓
Purchases figures for supplies received		
Hours worked by hourly paid employees		correct
Hours worked by employees paid on a piecework basis	✓	✗

Task 2

(a) Indicate with a tick in the appropriate column below which aspect of running a business best describes the activities listed in the left-hand column. Choose from:

(a) ensuring the smooth running of a business

(b) improving the solvency of a business

(c) compliance with legal requirements by the business

	smooth running ✔	improving solvency ✔	legal compliance ✔
Paying supplier invoices by the due date	✓		
Negotiating a longer payment period from suppliers		✓	
Avoiding fines by sending tax information promptly to HMRC		✓	
Sending the annual payroll return to HMRC			✓
Backing up computer files containing personal data	✓		
Keeping computer files containing personal data confidential			✓

(b) Solvency can be achieved by careful management of money and liquidity. State whether or not the following actions help improve solvency. Tick the appropriate box.

	yes ✔	no ✔
Accepting a high rate of settlement discount offered by suppliers		✓
Keeping a schedule of when your debts need to be repaid	✓	
Giving longer credit periods to customers to encourage sales		✓
Investing surplus cash in a bank account which offers a high rate of interest but requires six months notice of withdrawal		✓

(c) The accounting function, in order to maintain the solvency of a business, will need to carry out a number of actions. Indicate the appropriate options in the table below. Choose **three** options.

	✔
Know when debts are due for repayment	✓
Borrow at the lowest possible interest rates	✓
Avoid financial penalties, eg for late payment of tax	✓
Borrow for longer periods only, even if the interest rate is lower	
Draw up a detailed production budget	

(d) An employee meets a customer socially out of working hours. She tells the customer the credit limit given to another customer of the business. She will be in breach of:

	✔
Health & Safety at Work legislation	
Confidentiality	✓
Working Time Regulations	

Task 3

Your name is Fran Jordan and you are the Accounts Department Manager at Chippen Furniture. You are in the processing of drafting an email (shown below).

The email is a request to Carlo Aggiunto (carlo.aggiunto@chippenfurniture.co.uk), Assistant in the Sales and Marketing Department, to update and send the spreadsheet which shows the monthly comparative sales of products for this and last year. You need the figures urgently, by the end of the day.

You are to:

(a)   Insert the email address of the recipient in the appropriate box.

(b)   Complete the remaining boxes (they are numbered for reference) with the most appropriate and correctly spelt words or phrases from the lists shown below (also numbered for reference).

From   fran.jordan@chippenfurniture.co.uk

To   carlo.aggiunto@chippenfurniture.co.uk

Subject   Comparative sales figures (all products)

[1] Hi Carlo

Please send me   [2] as soon as possible   the latest sales spreadsheet

which shows the   [3] monthly   comparative figures for all

products. I need these figures   [4] by the end of today   .

[5] Thanks

Fran Jordan, Manager, Accounts Department

Option Lists
Pick one word or phrase for each numbered box from the following numbered lists:

1   Hi Carlo, Dear Carlo Aggiunto, Carlo, Hello Carlo, (box left blank)

2   a.s.a.p.,, as soon as possible, at your earliest convenience, without delay

3   monthly, annual, weekly, daily

4   immediately, sometime this week, tomorrow, by the end of today

5   Fanx, Thanks, Ta, With gratitude

Task 4

You are an Accounts Assistant employed by Piper Limited and work on the Purchase Ledger Section.

Your working hours are 09.00 to 17.00 with an hour for lunch from 13.00 to 14.00.

You have a staff meeting every Monday at 11.00 which is compulsory.

Your other duties during the week are set out on the schedule below.

Task description	Scheduling of tasks		Time taken
	Day	Time	for task
Dealing with emails and the post	Daily	9.00	1 hour
Processing purchase orders	Daily	10.00	1 hour
Processing returns to suppliers	Tuesday	11.00	2 hours
Inventory count	Wednesday	14.00	3 hours
Processing invoices from suppliers	Thursday	15.00	2 hours
Preparing cheque and BACS payments to suppliers	Friday	12.00	1 hour
Working at office of subsidiary company	Friday	14.00	3 hours

On Wednesday morning just before lunch you receive the following email from the Accounts Manager:

Hi Charlie

As you know I am currently carrying out the six-monthly staff appraisal interviews, but have been called away unexpectedly next week when your interview was scheduled.

Please can you come and see me at 2.00 pm tomorrow (Thursday) afternoon instead.

Please let me know if there is any problem.

Thanks

(a) As you are very busy at the moment, particularly in the middle of the week, this will need some time planning, but you should be able to do it if you prioritise your tasks. Tick the option below which seems to you the best solution in the circumstances.

✔

Ask your Union representative if this is acceptable practice.	
Email the Manager to ask if the appraisal could take place in a week or two when you are less busy.	
Do not reply to the email because you think it is an unreasonable request.	
Email the Manager to say that you will be able to attend the appraisal.	✓

✓

(b) Write a 'to do' list for Wednesday afternoon/Thursday set out below by listing the tasks in order of completion. Write the task descriptions in the column on the right.

Choose from the following tasks:

   Dealing with emails and the post

   Processing purchase orders

   Processing returns to suppliers

   Inventory count

   Processing invoices from suppliers

   Preparing cheque and BACS payments to suppliers

   Working at the office of subsidiary company

   Attending the appraisal interview

WEDNESDAY AFTERNOON/THURSDAY 'TO DO' LIST (in order of completion)	
Task 1	Inventory count 2 - 5
Task 2	dealing with email + the post 9-10
Task 3	processing purchase order 10-11
Task 4	processing invoices from supplier 11 - 1
Task 5	attend appraisal interview 2

✓

Task 5

You have been passed the following draft letter (to a Mr Pironi) to check.

There are five major errors which could include wrong spellings, bad grammar or the wrong use of words.

You are to:

(a) Identify the five incorrect words and enter them in the left-hand column of the table below.

(b) Enter your correction of these five words on the appropriate line in the right-hand column of the table below.

Dear Mr Peroni,

<u>Missing payment</u>

Thank you for your letter of 19 April.

We are sorry that you did not receive our payment of £1,200. It should of been sent by bank transfer on 22 March. It's reference number was 923829.

We are, of course, responsable for making sure the money is in your hands and will chase up the matter with our bank.

Yours faithfully,

---

incorrect word	correction
Peroni	Pironi
of	have
it's	its
responsable	responsible
faithfully	sincerely

Task 6

You work as an Accounts Assistant for Redweiller Limited, a wholesaler for petfoods and pet accessories. The company sells the petfoods and pet accessories mainly on credit to pet shops and other distributors.

Your main job is in the Sales Ledger section and you have responsibility for monitoring the credit accounts. You have to make sure that customers who are slow and late in paying are given plenty of reminders.

The normal credit terms given are payment within 30 days of invoice date.

At the end of October (year 20X2) you have been asked by the Accounts Manager for the figures for customer accounts outstanding over different time periods, ie up to 30 days, 31 to 60 days and 61 days or more. You are required to compare these figures with the figures for the same period last year.

The Accounts Manager is getting worried that although sales have nearly doubled since last year, an increasing number of accounts are not being settled by customers within the normal 30 days.

Your spreadsheet shows the following statistics:

Trade receivables – periods for accounts outstanding	20X1	20X2
	£	£
A	B	C
Trade receivables: Amounts outstanding 0-30 days	43,210	44,920
Trade receivables: Amounts outstanding 31-60 days	22,150	35,207
Trade receivables: Amounts outstanding 61 days and over	12,931	43,373
Total amount outstanding	78,291	123,500

In order to make the figures more easily understood you are to

(a)   Total up the figures for each year and enter the totals in the boxes on the bottom row of the table (columns B and C).

(b)   Using the table on the next page, work out for each time period the difference between this year's figure and last year's figure.

Enter the figures in Column D.

If the change is positive, write a plus sign before the figure.

(c) Using the difference figures you have arrived at in (b), calculate the percentage changes in amounts oustanding, ie the difference as a percentage of the 20X1 figure (Column B).

Enter all these percentages in Column E.

Percentages should be calculated to the nearest whole figure.

If the change is positive, write a plus sign before the figure; if it is negative, write a minus sign.

Receivables: time periods	20X1 £	20X2 £	difference £	percentage change
A	B	C	D	E
Outstanding 0-30 days	43,210	44,920	1710	– 4%
Outstanding 31-60 days	22,150	35,207	13,057	– 59%
Outstanding 61 days and over	12,931	43,373	30,442	– 235%

(d) Your manager asks you what effect an increase in the time a customer takes to pay up has on the solvency of the business. Tick the correct answer.

	✔
It improves solvency because you are owed money.	
It has a bad effect on solvency because cash is not coming in on time.	✓
It makes no difference at all.	

(e) How could Redweiller Limited best improve its credit control system? Tick the most appropriate answer.

	✔
Reduce the number of customers to whom it gives credit.	
Extend the the number of days credit that it gives to customers.	
Send out debt reminders more frequently and follow them up.	✓

Task 7

Your supervisor has recently reviewed your performance and identified your strengths and weaknesses. She has suggested a number of ways in which you can improve your performance (remedying weaknesses) and develop your skills (developing your strengths).

You are to match the strength and the weakness on the left with the appropriate improvement and development opportunities on the right. Draw two lines as appropriate.

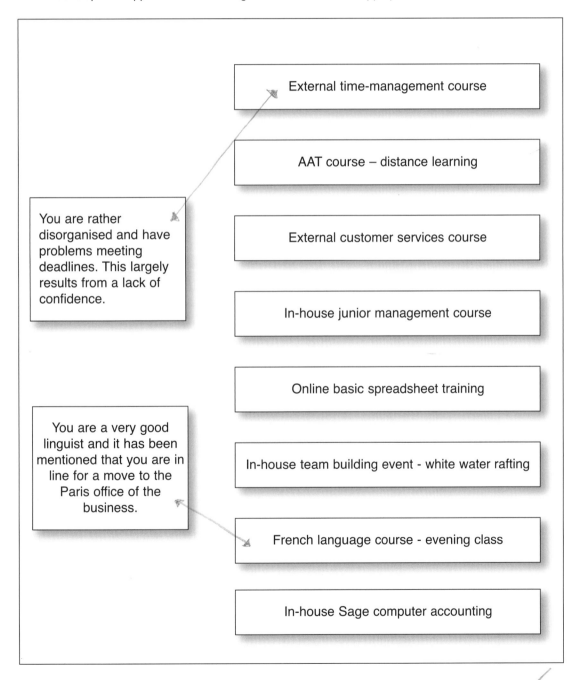

Task 8

(a) A business report normally contains seven sections, each with a distinct function. The seven sections are:

1 Title

2 Summary

3 Introduction

4 Findings

5 Conclusions

6 Recommendations

7 Appendices

You are to match the two sections on the left with the appropriate descriptions on the right. Draw two lines as appropriate.

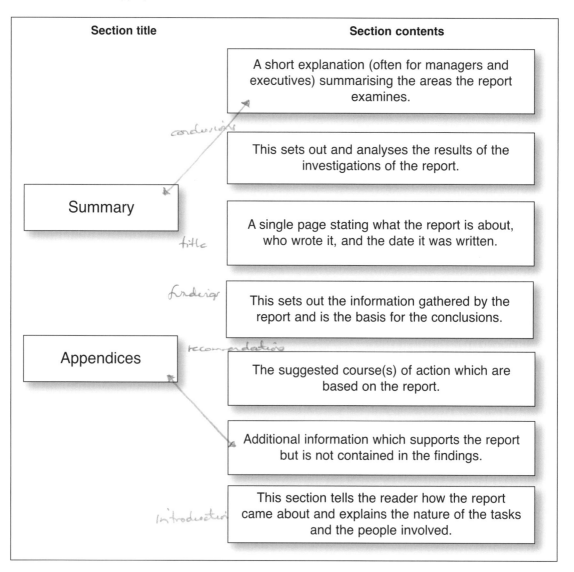

Section title | Section contents

A short explanation (often for managers and executives) summarising the areas the report examines.

This sets out and analyses the results of the investigations of the report.

Summary

A single page stating what the report is about, who wrote it, and the date it was written.

This sets out the information gathered by the report and is the basis for the conclusions.

Appendices

The suggested course(s) of action which are based on the report.

Additional information which supports the report but is not contained in the findings.

This section tells the reader how the report came about and explains the nature of the tasks and the people involved.

Task 8(b)

The Accounts Manager has asked for a Report to be drafted following an investigation into the credit control system of Rendell Limited. He has been told that a number of customers to whom the company sells on credit have become late payers, and a few have not paid at all and have been written off as irrecoverable (bad) debts. The investigation has extracted statistics from the ledger accounts for the last 3 years. The figures are shown in the table below. The latest year is Year 3.

Rendell Limited – late payers and irrecoverable (bad) debts			
	Year 1	**Year 2**	**Year 3**
Percentage of customers who paid late	14%	25%	34%
Annual sales	£392,500	£400,547	£434,932
Irrecoverable (bad) debts written off	£12,520	£26,500	£56,200

Calculate the percentage (to the nearest whole number) of annual sales which were written off as irrecoverable (bad) debt. The formula is (bad debts ÷ annual sales) x 100.

Year 1 | 3 % |

Year 2 | 7 % |

Year 3 | 13 % | ✓

(c) Select **TWO conclusions** to be included in the Report. Tick the appropriate boxes (✔).

The percentage of late payers remains very much the same.	
The percentage of late payers has gone down.	
The percentage of late payers has increased.	✓
Compared with the level of annual sales, the amount written off as irrecoverable (bad) debt has remained stable.	
Compared with the level of annual sales, the amount written off as irrecoverable (bad) debt has increased significantly.	✓
Compared with the level of annual sales, the amount written off as irrecoverable (bad) debt has decreased.	

✓

Task 8(d)

Select **TWO recommendations** to be included in the Report. Tick the appropriate boxes.

✔

Increase the number of the debt chasers we send to customers and exercise stricter control if a customer exceeds the credit limit.	✓
Allow our customers longer periods of credit, as that will reduce the need to chase up the debts so frequently.	
Reduce the number of irrecoverable (bad) debts we write off in the hope that the customers will eventually pay up.	
Reduce the number of irrecoverable (bad) debts through stricter credit control when customers exceed their limits.	✓

Task 9

(a) Reporting lines within an organisation can be (choose **one** option):

	✔
Upwards only	
Upwards and downwards only	
Horizontal only	
Upwards and downwards and horizontal	✓

(b) Accounts assistants are most likely to report directly and on a frequent basis to (choose **one** option):

	✔
The finance director	
An accounts department line manager	✓
A line manager in another department	
An external auditor	

(c) Problems and conflicts at work will need to be resolved. Sometimes they can be sorted out personally with an individual, sometimes they will need to be referred to a line manager. Assume that you are an Accounts Assistant and indicate below which issues can be resolved by you, and which will need to be referred to a line manager.

	✔ you	✔ manager
You overhear your line manager saying that your standard of work is below what he expects. Your mother is very ill and you are helping to look after her.		✓
You are aware that a colleague is taking other people's biscuits and pot noodles from the office kitchen.	✓	
A colleague is constantly making loud racist remarks.		✓

Work effectively in accounting

Practice assessment 1 answers

Task 1

(a)

Emergency procedures for fire	✔
Disciplinary procedures	✔
Clothing worn on the production line	
The use of environmentally friendly cleaning materials	

(b)

The Production Department	
The tax authorities	✔
Its competitors	
The bank	✔

(c)

Complete, mostly accurate and produced as quickly as possible	
Complete, accurate and on time	✔
Mostly complete, accurate and on time	

Task 2

(a)

	smooth running ✔	improving solvency ✔	legal compliance ✔
Processing the payroll in good time	✔		
Sending out customer statements on time		✔	
Sending out payment to suppliers at the latest possible date		✔	
Complying with Health & Safety regulations			✔
Ensuring that there is no sex discrimination at work			✔
Keeping the filing up-to-date	✔		

(b)

The balance of money in the bank account	
Being able to pay debts when they are due	✔
Keeping up to date with paying suppliers	
Obtaining the best return on money invested for the long term	

(c)

Share capital of a company owned by its employees	
The balance of money kept in a bank account	
Day-to-day funds available to a business	✔
Money due from customers plus money due to suppliers	

(d)

situation	area of legislation, or 'not applicable'
Eyestrain experienced by a computer operator	Health & Safety at Work
An employee with very bad breath which annoys other people in the workplace	not applicable
An employee who provides his address to the employer's Human Resources Department for internal use.	not applicable
An employee who provides the address of a customer to another business	Data Protection
An employee accidentally washes her hands in bleach in the staff kitchen and burns her hands	Health & Safety at Work
An employee cycling to work accidentally runs into a pedestrian who is then injured	not applicable
An employee receives a telephone call from a local radio station wanting the name and address of an employee who has won a prize in a competition	Data Protection

Task 3

From	sam.sung@crocus.co.uk
To	nthacker@crocus.co.uk
Subject	March payroll data

Hi Nishit

Please send me the hours worked by | all employees by department |

for the month of | March | **3** . It would be useful if you could send

me this data on the usual spreadsheet. I need the information by | 5 April. |

Many thanks

Sam

Payroll, Accounts Department

Task 4

(a)

THURSDAY 'TO DO' LIST (in order of completion)	
Task 1	Dealing with emails and the post
Task 2	Processing sales orders
Task 3	Sales invoicing and credit notes on Sage
Task 4	Preparing and sending out customer statements
Task 5	Updating the office filing

(b)

If statements or chaser letters are sent out late this would adversely affect the cash flow of the business.	✔
Processing of payments received from customers would be delayed.	
The overdue account letters might not be produced on time.	✔
The office filing might be delayed.	
The post may not get opened.	
The statements might not be produced on time.	✔

Task 5

incorrect word	correction
Jeliowski	Joliewski
inclosed	enclosed
what	which
recieved	received
faithfully	sincerely

Task 6

(a)

£1,491,100

(b)

27.53%

(c)

54.04%

(d)

18.43%

(e) & (f)

Region	Revised Sales (£) January- March
South	356,400
West	349,340
North	410,520
East	374,840
Total sales	1,491,100

(g)

23.90%

(h)

25.14%

(i)   The sales percentage of the South region has decreased and the sales percentage of the East region has increased.

Task 7

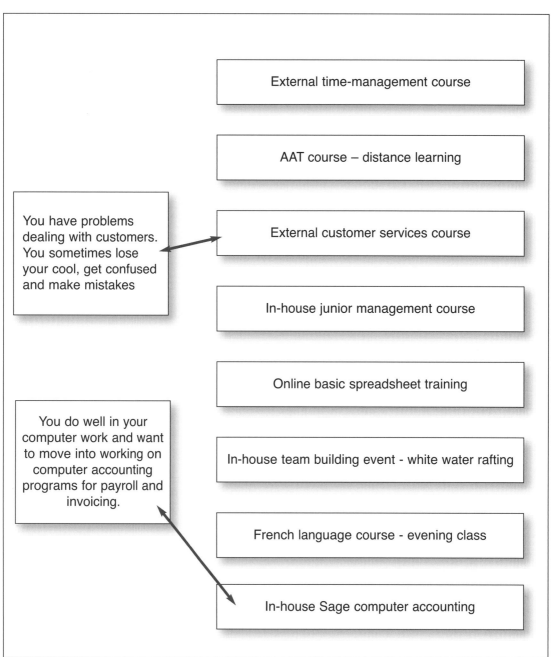

Task 8

(a)

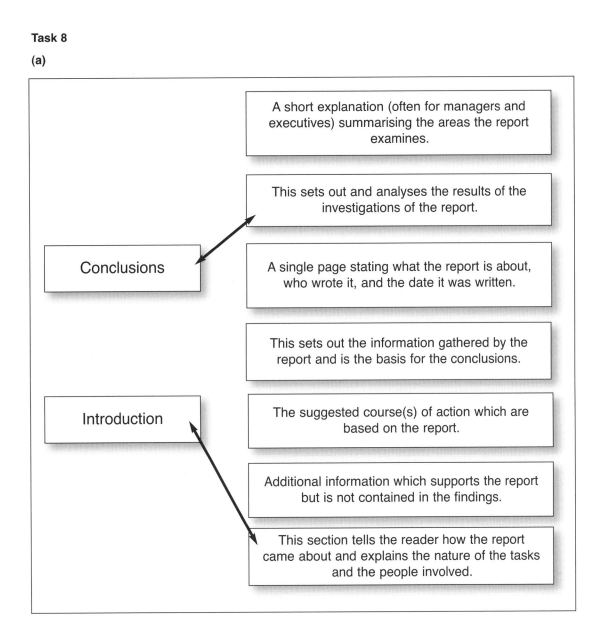

(b) 1 & 2

PENTOLA LIMITED – 3 YEAR PAYROLL COST AND AVERAGE COST PER YEAR				
Payroll system used	Total annual running cost (3 x annual running cost) £	Set-up cost £	Total cost for 3 years £	Average annual cost £
Manual payroll (in-house)	4,000 x 3 = 12,000	0	12,000	4,000
Computerised payroll (in-house)	1,200 x 3 = 3,600	7,500	11,100	3,700
Payroll bureau (external)	5,000 x 3 = 15,000	0	15,000	5,000

(c) The computerised payroll system is the cheapest option over the three years.

It would be a good idea to use the computerised payroll option because the set-up costs are only a 'one-off' expense and the long-term total costs are lower.

(d) Call a meeting of Accounts staff and explain to them the benefits using a computerised accounting system and promise them suitable training.

Draw up a plan for the extra computer equipment that will be needed and obtain further information about computer accounting training courses.

Task 9

(a)

Purchase Ledger Assistants only	
Assistants in the Accounting Department only	
Assistants from a variety of Departments	✔

(b)

Payroll Assistants only	
Payroll and other Assistants	✔
The Accounts Manager	

(c)

Keep quiet and hope that the error will not be noticed	
Report the problem direct to the Finance Director	
Report the problem to her Line Manager	✔

(d)

	by you	by a manager
A colleague keeps taking your crisps	✔	
A colleague keeps taking office postage stamps		✔
A colleague has bad body odour	✔	

Work effectively in accounting

Practice assessment 2 answers

Task 1

(a)

Working under the influence of alcohol or drugs	
Applying the correct VAT rate to an invoice	✔
Using a work computer to access pornographic material	
Using a work computer to send private emails.	

(b)

Stakeholder	Accounting information
HM Revenue & Customs	Cash available to repay loans
Bank	Checking supplier invoices
Suppliers	VAT figures
	Credit record for payment of trade debts
	Payroll calculations
	Petty cash book

(c)

Recording orders received, producing invoices, producing credit notes	✔
Recording orders made, receiving invoices, checking credit notes	
Checking orders received, producing invoices, checking payments received	

Task 2

(a)

	smooth running ✔	improving solvency ✔	legal compliance ✔
Paying supplier invoices by the due date	✔		
Negotiating a longer payment period from suppliers		✔	
Avoiding fines by sending tax information promptly to HMRC		✔	
Sending the employer annual payroll return to HMRC			✔
Backing up computer files containing personal data	✔		
Keeping computer files containing personal data confidential			✔

(b)

	yes ✔	no ✔
Chasing up overdue customer accounts	✔	
Giving customers longer credit periods		✔
Paying suppliers as soon as possible		✔
Paying suppliers as late as possible	✔	

(c)

	positive ✔	negative ✔
an increase in the average payment period given to credit customers		✔
an increase in the average payment period given by suppliers	✔	
a business pays cheques received into the bank every day	✔	
a business increases its trade discounts to its customers		✔

(d)

Health & Safety at Work legislation	
The Highway Code	
Working Time Regulations	✔

Task 3

From	rmorgan@delphiansoftware.co.uk

To   rsingh@delphiansoftware.co.uk

Subject credit control meeting   **1**

Hello Ranveer

We are holding a meeting to discuss   credit control systems   **2**

on   13 July at 11.30   **3**   . This meeting will be held in the

No. 2 Conference Room   **4**   . It would be very helpul if you could attend.

Many thanks and kind regards

Riley Morgan

Accounts Department

Task 4

(a)

Email to say that your work schedule will not allow you to do the task in time.	
Reply to say that you will have the figures for him if you can do overtime on Thursday evening.	
Confirm that you will have the figures for him in time for his meeting on Friday.	✔
Do not reply to him but just hope that you can provide the figures in time.	

(b)

FRIDAY 'TO DO' LIST (in order of completion)	
Task 1	Dealing with emails and the post
Task 2	Preparing account information for Gerda Construction Ltd
Task 3	Processing sales invoices
Task 4	Listing the cheques and cash for paying in at the bank
Task 5	Paying in at the bank

Task 5

incorrect word	correction
Extenson	Extension
4	for
advice	advise
neccesary	necessary
ammendments	amendments

Task 6

      (a)   70,400

      (b)   22%

      (c)   52%

      (d)   26%

      (e)   Fourlander

      (f)   £1,595 each

      (g)   greater than the total of Sportstars and Whizzes added together

Task 7

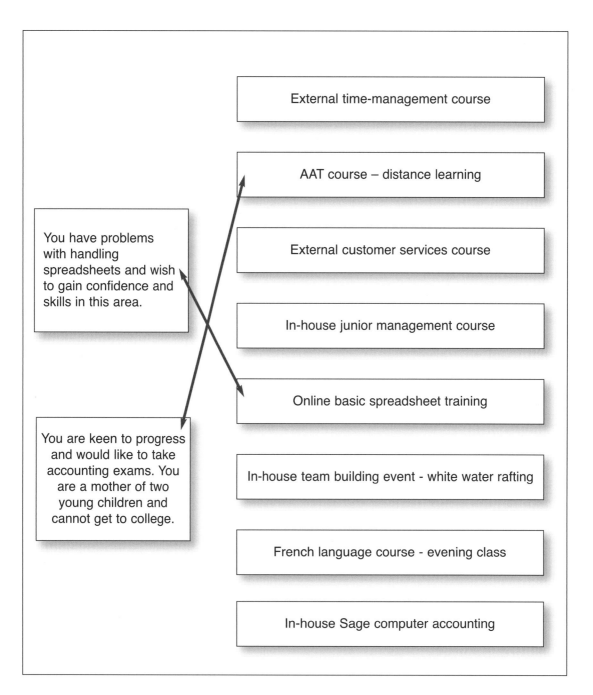

You have problems with handling spreadsheets and wish to gain confidence and skills in this area.

You are keen to progress and would like to take accounting exams. You are a mother of two young children and cannot get to college.

External time-management course

AAT course – distance learning

External customer services course

In-house junior management course

Online basic spreadsheet training

In-house team building event - white water rafting

French language course - evening class

In-house Sage computer accounting

Task 8

(a)

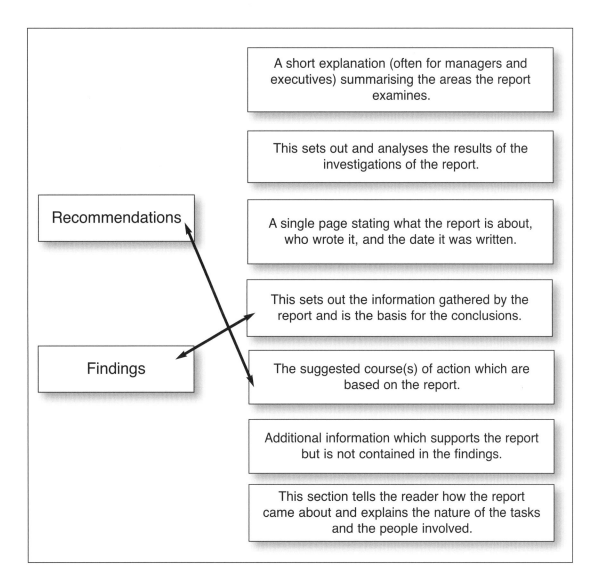

(b)

RESULTS OF CUSTOMER SERVICE QUESTIONNAIRE (ACCOUNTS DEPARTMENT)			
Question	Good %	Satisfactory %	Unsatisfactory %
How do you rate our customer service for politeness and readiness to help?	80	16	4
How well informed about our services and systems are the staff that you speak to?	48	28	24
How easy is it to get through the main switchboard to the Accounts Department?	20	32	48

(c)   The results for customer service for politeness were good.

Staff knowledge of service and systems was at fault in a number of instances.

Many customers found it difficult in getting through the main switchboard to the Accounts Department.

(d)

Take no action immediately but send out the questionnaire to another group of customers after six months.	
Timetable training sessions for Accounts staff in order to improve their technical knowledge, and suggest they enrol for an AAT course.	✔
Consult with the managerial staff in charge of the main company switchboard and ask that urgent action be taken to improve the service provided to customers.	✔
Suggest that customers are encouraged to send in emails rather than use the telephone to contact the Accounts Department staff.	

Task 9

(a)

Finance Director	✔
Sales Director	
Financial Accountant	
Payroll Manager	

(b)

Sales Manager	
Purchase Ledger Supervisor	
Accounts Manager	✔
Cashier	

(c)

	by you	by manager
A colleague has a habit of asking you to finish the invoicing when she has to go to meet her boyfriend.	✔	
Your line manager assumes you are trained in spreadsheets but you are not and you have problems in trying to use them.		✔
A colleague is consistently making mistakes which reflects badly on your own work.		✔

Work effectively in accounting

Practice assessment 3 answers

Task 1

(a)

Authorisation limits for the signing of cheques	
Authorisation limits for ordering goods and services	
Setting the tax codes issued for calculating employees' pay	✔
Operation of the petty cash system	

(b)

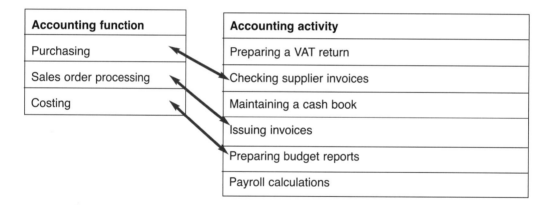

Accounting function		Accounting activity
Purchasing		Preparing a VAT return
Sales order processing		Checking supplier invoices
Costing		Maintaining a cash book
		Issuing invoices
		Preparing budget reports
		Payroll calculations

(c)

Sales figures for sales reps who work on a commission basis	✔
Purchases figures for supplies received	
Hours worked by hourly paid employees	✔
Hours worked by employees paid on a piecework basis	

Task 2

(a)

	smooth running ✔	improving solvency ✔	legal compliance ✔
Paying supplier invoices by the due date	✔		
Negotiating a longer payment period from suppliers		✔	
Avoiding fines by sending tax information promptly to HMRC		✔	
Sending the annual payroll return to HMRC			✔
Backing up computer files containing personal data	✔		
Keeping computer files containing personal data confidential			✔

(b)

	yes ✔	no ✔
accepting a high rate of settlement discount offered by suppliers	✔	
keeping a schedule of when your debts need to be repaid	✔	
giving longer credit periods to customers to encourage sales		✔
investing surplus cash in a bank account which offers a high rate of interest but requires six months notice of withdrawal		✔

(c)

Know when debts are due for repayment	✔
Borrow at the lowest possible interest rates	✔
Avoid financial penalties, eg for late payment of tax	✔
Borrow for longer periods only, even if the interest rate is lower	
Draw up a detailed production budget	

(d)

Health & Safety at Work legislation	
Confidentiality	✔
Working Time Regulations	

Task 3

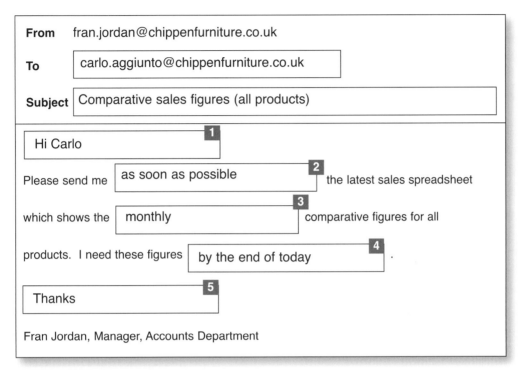

From   fran.jordan@chippenfurniture.co.uk

To   carlo.aggiunto@chippenfurniture.co.uk

Subject   Comparative sales figures (all products)

Hi Carlo **1**

Please send me | as soon as possible | **2** the latest sales spreadsheet

which shows the | monthly | **3** comparative figures for all

products. I need these figures | by the end of today | **4** .

Thanks **5**

Fran Jordan, Manager, Accounts Department

Notes – alternative answers

This task is about using informal language which should not become too familiar or 'text speak'. Some of the boxes could arguably have more than one 'informal' answer:

Box 1   Alternatives could include similar informal greetings: 'Carlo' or 'Hello Carlo'

Box 2   'a.s.a.p' is an alternative, but is not as clear as the actual words.

Task 4

(a)

Ask your Union representative if this is acceptable practice.	
Email the Manager to ask if the appraisal could take place in a week or two when you are less busy.	
Do not reply to the email because you think it is an unreasonable request.	
Email the Manager to say that you will be able to attend the appraisal.	✔

(b)

WEDNESDAY/THURSDAY 'TO DO' LIST (in order of completion)	
Task 1	Inventory count
Task 2	Dealing with emails and the post
Task 3	Processing purchase orders
Task 4	Processing invoices from suppliers
Task 5	Attending the appraisal interview

Task 5

incorrect word	correction
Peroni	Pironi
of	have
it's	its
responsable	responsible
faithfully	sincerely

Task 6

(a)

Trade receivables – periods for accounts outstanding	20X1 £	20X2 £
A	B	C
Trade receivables: Amounts outstanding 0-30 days	43,210	44,920
Trade receivables: Amounts outstanding 31-60 days	22,150	35,207
Trade receivables: Amounts outstanding 61 days and over	12,931	43,373
Total amount outstanding	78,291	123,500

(b) & (c)

Receivables: time periods	20X1 £	20X2 £	difference £	percentage change
A	B	C	D	E
Outstanding 0-30 days	43,210	44,920	+ 1,710	+ 4%
Outstanding 31-60 days	22,150	35,207	+ 13,057	+ 59%
Outstanding 61 days and over	12,931	43,373	+ 30,442	+ 235%

(d)   It has a bad effect on solvency because cash is not coming in on time.

(e)   Send out debt reminders more frequently and follow them up.

Task 7

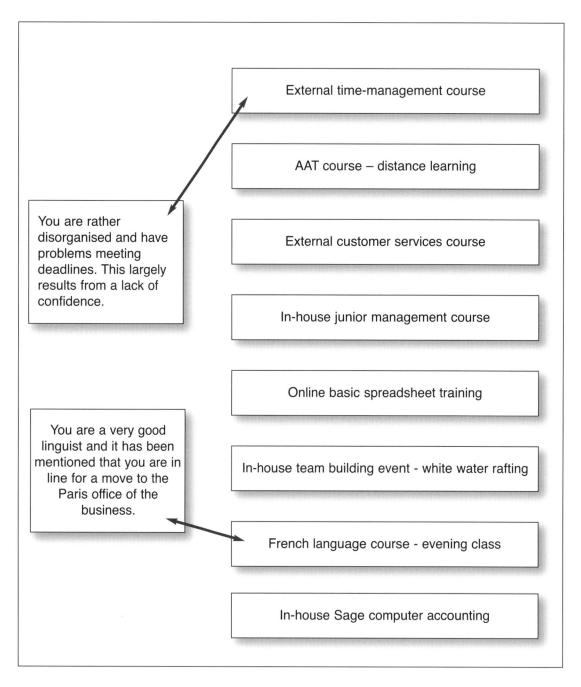

Task 8 (a)

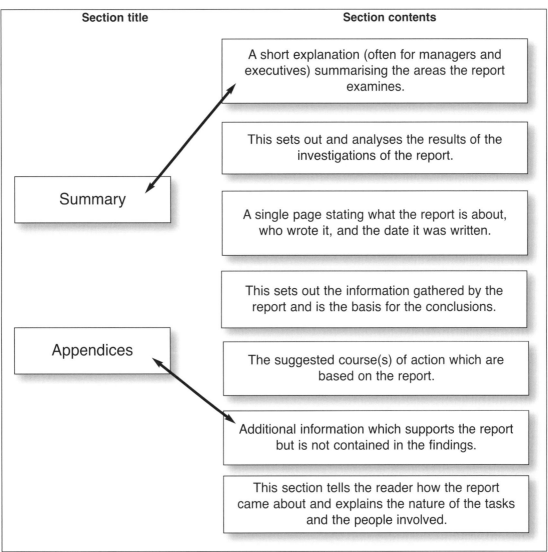

Section title

Section contents

A short explanation (often for managers and executives) summarising the areas the report examines.

This sets out and analyses the results of the investigations of the report.

Summary

A single page stating what the report is about, who wrote it, and the date it was written.

This sets out the information gathered by the report and is the basis for the conclusions.

Appendices

The suggested course(s) of action which are based on the report.

Additional information which supports the report but is not contained in the findings.

This section tells the reader how the report came about and explains the nature of the tasks and the people involved.

(b)   Year 1, 3%; Year 2, 7%; Year 3, 13%

(c)   The percentage of late payers has increased.

Compared with the level of annual sales, the amount written off as irrecoverable (bad) debt has increased significantly.

(d)   Increase the number of the debt chasers we send to customers and exercise stricter control if a customer exceeds the credit limit.

Reduce the number of irrecoverable (bad) debts through stricter credit control when customers exceed their limits.

Task 9

(a)

Upwards only	
Upwards and downwards only	
Horizontal only	
Upwards and downwards and horizontal	✔

(b)

The finance director	
An accounts department line manager	✔
A line manager in another department	
An external auditor	

(c)

	you	manager
You overhear your line manager saying that your standard of work is below what he expects. Your mother is very ill and you are helping to look after her.		✔
You are aware that a colleague is taking other people's biscuits and pot noodles from the office kitchen.	✔	
A colleague is constantly making loud racist remarks.		✔